REPORT
2005
A MAN'S GUIDE TO WOMEN

REPORT
2005

A MAN'S GUIDE TO WOMEN

THE SECRET TRICKS AND EXPERT TECHNIQUES
EVERY GUY NEEDS TO GET THE SEX HE WANTS

RODALE

Sex and Values at Rodale

We believe that an active and healthy sex life, based on mutual consent and respect between partners, is an important component of physical and mental well-being. We also respect that sex is a private matter and that each person has a different opinion of what sexual practices or levels of discourse are appropriate. Rodale is committed to offering responsible, practical advice about sexual matters, supported by accredited professionals and legitimate scientific research. Our goal—for sex and all other topics—is to publish information that empowers people's lives.

Mention of specific companies, organizations, or authorities in this book does not imply endorsement by the author or publisher, nor does mention of specific companies, organizations, or authorities imply that they endorse this book, its author, or the publisher.

Internet addresses and telephone numbers given in this book were accurate at the time it went to press.

© 2005 by Rodale Inc.
Photographs © by Digital Vision (xii, 40, 62), Digital Vision/Getty Images (110), Justin Pumfrey/Getty Images (146), Michelangelo Gratton/Getty Images (210)

Printed in the United States of America
Rodale Inc. makes every effort to use acid-free ∞, recycled paper ♻.

Men's Health is a registered trademark of Rodale Inc.

Book design by Joanna Williams

ISBN-13 978-1-59486-084-3 hardcover
ISBN-10 1-59486-084-X hardcover

2 4 6 8 10 9 7 5 3 1   hardcover

Visit us on the Web at www.menshealthbooks.com, or call us toll-free at (800) 848-4735.

RODALE

WE **INSPIRE** AND **ENABLE** PEOPLE TO IMPROVE
THEIR LIVES AND THE WORLD AROUND THEM

FOR MORE OF OUR PRODUCTS
WWW.RODALESTORE.COM
(800) 848-4735

Report 2005: A Man's Guide to Women Staff

Executive Editor: Jeremy Katz
Editor: Daniel Listwa
Contributing Writers: Marla Abramson, Nicole Beland, Jennifer
     Benjamin, Daniella Brodsky, Heather Buchanan, Chris Connolly,
     Samantha Daniels, Kathryn Eisman, Bruce Jay Friedman, Ron
     Geraci, Siski Green, Sarah Hepola, Lisa Jones, Christopher
     McDougall, Sarah Miller, Daniel Asa Rose, Elissa Schappell,
     Allison Winn Scotch, Amy Sohn, Ted Spiker, Laurence Roy
     Stains, Bill Stieg, Caroline Tiger, Amy Jo Van Bodegraven, Mike
     Zimmerman
Interior and Cover Designer: Joanna Williams
Photo Editor: Darlene Malkames
Project Editor: Lois Hazel
Copy Editor: Anne Winthrop Esposito
Layout Designer: Faith Hague
Product Specialist: Jodi Schaffer
Senior Managing Editor: Chris Krogermeier
Vice President, Art Director: Andy Carpenter
Managing Art Director: Darlene Schneck
Vice President, Publisher, Direct Response Books: Gregg Michaelson
Senior Director, Direct Response Marketing: Janine Slaughter
Product Manager: Matthew Neumaier

CONTENTS

Part 6: Hot Monogamy

INTRODUCTION

I've seen plenty of offbeat sexual tips, facts and studies this year, but my favorite arrived in August: in a study of 16,000 Americans, the National Bureau of Economic Research determined that people who have sex are happier than Americans who don't have sex.

A study like this begs a number of questions. Why is the National Bureau of *Economic Research* surveying Americans about sex? If the NBER is focusing on sex, is anyone focusing on the economy?

But the most important question is this:

Do guys really need a major survey to tell us the path to happiness is through our pants?

It's moments like these when I'm most proud of *A Man's Guide to Women*. Inside, you'll find 250 + pages of information you can actually use: up-to-date, reliable advice for meeting, mingling, and mating with the woman of your choice. The kind of stuff even an economist can't teach.

For example, you'll learn:

• **THE 30 THINGS EVERY WOMAN WANTS YOU TO KNOW.** The logic here is that if you make her happy, she'll gladly make *you* happy.

• **A SERIAL SEDUCER'S RULES FOR GETTING THE GIRLS OF YOUR DREAMS.** He's a dog groomer by profession, but a ladies' man at heart. Learn how this very average guy seals the deal, and how you can too.

• **HOW TO UN-BREAK HER HEART.** Made a mistake that destroyed your relationship? You can rebuild it. We'll teach you how.

• **THE SIX EROGENOUS ZONES YOU CAN'T AFFORD TO NEGLECT.** You know all the usual hot-buttons, but what about the ones you're missing? Press these, and prepare for an explosion.

• **HOW TO ACT WHEN SHE'S ON THE ATTACK.** A must-read for any guy who has ever had to calm an overemotional/annoyed/brooding girl.

• **THE FAIL-SAFE GUIDE TO SPOTTING A CHEAT.** Think she's faithful? Maybe . . . but maybe not. Read and find out.

You already know what makes you happy. Now learn how to get it. Enjoy the Report.

—DANIEL LISTWA
EDITOR

GUY KNOWLEDGE

Ever dabbled in Boy Scouting? If you're ashamed to admit it, we understand—it's hard to defend those short pants, kerchiefs, and all those hours spent building pinewood stock cars. Then again, Boy Scouts have a leg up on other guys if they live the Boy Scout motto: "Be Prepared."

In the world of women, being prepared means arming yourself with enough guy smarts to navigate tricky sexual terrain. If you have to defend a promiscuous past, you're prepared. If that pretty-but-slightly-crazy gal in accounting asks *you* out, but expects you to pay, you're prepared. If your wife is ready but your erection isn't able? You guessed it: You're prepared.

Luckily, you won't have to go far to earn a merit badge for sexual intelligence. We've crammed enough guy knowledge into the chapters ahead to fill 1,000 pup tents. All you have to do is turn the page.

Prepared? You will be.

What She Wishes You Knew about Her

Universal truths all men should understand
about women   BY HEATHER BUCHANAN

1. She'll yell at you to pick up your dirty clothes but steal your sweaty T-shirt to sleep in when you're gone.

2. She knows that roses seem cliché, but she melts inside when you send them to her.

3. She'll fight to the end to maintain her independence but fantasizes about you taking care of her.

4. It's cheating as soon as you're doing something with another woman that you wouldn't want her to see, hear, read. . . .

5. When you do something bad and she seems cool with it, she's not.

6. She'd love to cook for you but fears Le Cirque does it better.

7. She's afraid she'll never find a purer love than her daddy's love.

8. When you push her hair behind her ears and look into her eyes and hold your lips over hers, she can't breathe.

9. She has no idea how to be strong and still say "I'm sorry."

10. She can love you and hate your guts at the same time.

11. She longs to receive a handwritten love letter.

12. When you ask her what's wrong and she says nothing, she wants you to keep questioning her.

13. She doesn't want you to solve her problems . . . just listen to them.

14. She holds on to an inner life and her own mysteries that she does not want to share.

15. She'll admire a beautiful woman before you will.

16. She loves when you draw a bath for her without her asking.

17. She wants you to go out with the guys more than you do. Really, she does.

18. Her biggest fear is that you will die before she does.

19. When it comes to aesthetics, she wants your enthusiasm, not your opinion.

20. She watches you when you sleep.

21. *Monday Night Football = Trading Spaces.*

22. She sides with Carly Simon over James Taylor.

23. She wants to know that you are vulnerable to her feminine wiles.

24. She wants you to celebrate her moves, not say, "Wow, you dance like Veronica—you know, from Archie."

25. Baby talk good; dirty talk better.

26. She likes expensive floral arrangements when you screw up (and when you don't).

27. She wants you to probe her nightmares and make them go away.

28. She'd like it if you dueted "Summer Lovin'" with her at a karaoke bar.

29. She'd love you to get into a bar brawl to defend her honor.

30. She thinks about sex more than you do.

The New Sex Pills

America has been invaded by two new drugs touted as the perfect pick-me-ups for the impotent man. Here's a sneak preview of how they can help you come up big in the bedroom

BY CHRISTOPHER McDOUGALL

FRANTIC, HIS PENIS FEELING AS IF it had just been skewered by a soldering iron, Keith Henderson raced around the apartment in search of relief, finally jamming his package into a jug of ice water. Ahh . . . his member turned ember was extinguished. And 2 seconds later, it was blazing again.

"I was hopping around," he recalls, "while my wife was falling off the bed laughing."

The real punch line: Keith had just tried to treat his erectile dysfunction. When even Viagra left him limp, he'd reached for the heavy artillery and decided to blast his penis with Muse, the last-resort syringe system that shoots a tiny medicated pellet straight into the urethra. That got a reaction.

"It felt as if someone was blasting me with a butane torch," Keith says one afternoon in the back office of his London picture-framing shop. He tells the story in the kind of awed, awful whisper combat vets use to describe their flashbacks, trying to keep his voice at a pitch the shopgirls out front can't hear, while still doing justice to the sensation that felt like having his scrotum dangled over the business end of a Zippo.

At age 44, Keith was about to surrender to his doctor's grim prediction that diabetes and two back operations might have extinguished his sex life for good. From the look of him, it's hard to imagine that such a trim, vibrant guy could be missing any vital functions. But even though he's a leather-lean 6'1" and 160 pounds—thanks to hectic workdays that have him hauling and installing heavy pictures in offices all over London—he's lost the bounce where it counts. "When I told my doctor Viagra wasn't helping, he didn't hold out much hope," Keith says. "Imagine what that did to my self-esteem. Imagine what it was doing to my marriage."

Luckily, neither suffered very long. A few months later, Keith happened to hear about a new erection wonder drug, Cialis, when he dropped by to do a favor for a friend working at London's Impotence Institute. His first reaction was outrage: "Why didn't my doctor know about this?" His second was resolve: "I have to get some." Since his urologist wasn't up to speed on Cialis, Keith called around until he found a fellow diabetic who agreed to slip him a few pills. "In my doctor's office, there wasn't a single piece of literature on these drugs, so I decided to take things into—sorry about this, but it's the only way to put it—my own hands."

Trying it, however, would be a little risky. Because he lives in England—one of the countries, along with South Africa and most of western Europe, where Cialis made its worldwide debut in February 2003—Keith would be among the first consumers in the world to sample the drug. True, his recent genital scalding had pretty much killed his taste for adventure, but he was feeling desperate. Within an hour of swallowing the pear-shaped yellow pill, Keith got that old, familiar punch in his pants and surprised his wife, Florence, with something she hadn't seen in 2 years.

"She was nearly petrified," he says sympathetically before giving way to a Vlad the Impaler cackle. (What the hell, she did crack up when his bits were burning.) "After so long with nothing, all of a sudden—*BAM!*—I'm standing there with a full-blown erection." Cialis not only gave Keith and his wife the first roll in the hay they'd enjoyed in years but also provided the second and third: Unlike Viagra, which wears off in about 4 hours, Cialis keeps on rocking for up to 36. (It's earned the nickname "Le Weekend" in Europe.)

You'd think three wife-jolting *BAM!*s in one night would make him a Cialis customer for life, but Keith soon moved on to a newer erection aid, called Levitra (this time legitimately; he found a new doctor). Introduced in the United Kingdom about a month after Cialis, Levitra caught his attention when he heard it was more potent than Cialis. He wasn't disappointed. Only 30 minutes after taking his first dose, Keith was smiling and Florence was wide-eyed all over again.

"Just wait till you get this new stuff in America," says Keith, on fire again, but this time with a prophet's joy. "You're going to love it!"

The wait is over. Both Levitra (manufactured by GlaxoSmith-Kline and Bayer) and Cialis (a Lilly ICOS product) are now available in the United States.

While a few guys may still be unfamiliar with Levitra, there aren't many men who don't already know about (and fear) erectile dysfunction (ED). It's basically a matter of hydraulics—blood isn't flowing into the penis. Sometimes the breakdown is psychological, with the brain deactivating the open-the-floodgates command because of stress or anxiety. Other times the cause is neurological, with nerve damage interrupting the critical command. But most often it's pure mechanics: Because of vascular problems, the cavernosal arteries—the paths by which blood fills the penis—become narrowed, turning what should be a love flood into a slow trickle.

A fix wasn't available until 1998. Pfizer chemists discovered that sildenafil citrate, a.k.a. Viagra, inhibited the body's levels of an enzyme called PDE-5, causing the cavernosal arteries to expand temporarily.

Even better, this expansion caused a corresponding constriction of the cavernosal veins, thereby preventing the erection-building blood from immediately draining back out. The result: erections. Ones with staying power.

Viagra, of course, was soon a high-five-the-headboard success. More than 80 percent of the men who tried it reported dramatic improvement. Stories abounded of marriages saved and shattered confidence restored. Viagra was such a miracle worker, in fact, that it was hard to believe when another statistic crept into the medical journals: Nearly 50 percent of men quit using the drug after 1 year.

No doubt side effects—severe headaches, flushing, blurry vision—were partly to blame, but a bigger factor may have simply been the hassle of taking Viagra. "Americans are used to instant convenience," says Myron Murdock, M.D., medical director of the Impotence Institute of America and a former chief resident in urology at Boston University. "We want that with our drugs; we want that with our sex." Using Viagra, however, takes very careful planning: You have to avoid fatty foods before taking it . . . then wait 2 hours after eating . . . wait another hour for it to kick in . . . have direct sexual stimulation . . . and if you don't wrap up the action in 5 hours, you can expect your steel-toed boot to change, Cinderella style, back into a loafer.

No wonder Dr. Murdock's patients are buzzing him with phone calls every day, asking when they can get their hands on Levitra and Cialis. (The United States is often the last to see new drugs because of its stringent approval process.) "The new drugs are much more potent and efficient," explains Dr. Murdock, who did clinical testing of Levitra by running double-blind studies on dozens of his patients. "They're designed to focus more specifically on the PDE-5 enzyme system, which means you get more power and fewer side effects." He's most impressed by case studies he's read about Levitra's having helped men—such as those with severe cases of diabetes—with hard-to-treat impotence.

But for all the medical reports and double-blind studies, no one can rank the new erection aids better than the users themselves. By now Keith Henderson has compared all three medications in their own penis-pill Pepsi challenge to see which one will best jump-start his stalled sex life. Here's how the drugs, and the men, measured up.

"Viagra gave me one hell of a stinking headache the second time I took it," says Roger Hyland, an otherwise fighting-fit 43-year-old officer in the British Royal Navy who spends his onshore time in the Portsmouth bungalow he shares with his wife, Alyson. "Kind of defeated the purpose, you know?" It was frustrating—on his first go with Viagra, Alyson said the sex was "brilliant." But when they tried again a few days later, sinus pain spread across Roger's skull and lasted as long as the drug's 5-hour activation time. Same thing happened the third time. There wasn't a fourth.

What bothered Roger most, however, was the effect the situation was having on his wife. "Ever since he started having ED problems, I tried to reassure myself that it wasn't me," says Alyson. For the first 6 months or so, they didn't even talk about it—not with each other, not even with lifelong friends. Even now, months later, it's a raw subject, one Roger feels comfortable discussing only by phone.

When he finally sought help from a doctor—Simon Holmes, M.D., a urologist and an erectile dysfunction specialist at St. Mary's Hospital in Portsmouth—Roger thought Viagra would solve the problem. But when he said he still couldn't perform because of the headaches, Alyson couldn't help wondering if he wasn't really losing desire for her.

"I've seen erectile dysfunction tear relationships apart," says Dr. Holmes, one of the few specialists in the area dealing with ED. (He currently has a 6-month waiting list for appointments.) "Often, it's not the lack of sex; it's the lack of confidence, in both partners." Dr. Holmes had a patient who'd been treated 8 years earlier for high blood pressure, except no one told him the medication could also make him impotent. Confused, miserable, the man started drinking and eventually lost his job and his family. It took nearly a decade for him to finally see a doctor, discover the truth, and turn his life around. "Viagra did wonders for him," says Dr. Holmes. "And that story is not uncommon."

But for all the emotional good they can do, impotence meds have a potential downside: Once you swallow one, you're supposed to be fully operational again, with no medical excuses to fall back on. Bob Dole could smirk all he wanted while hawking Viagra, but you can bet that in private, once he'd downed the drug, he started hearing the same unnerving drumbeat that pounds in the back of many men's minds: When is it going to work? What if it doesn't work?

"There's an absolutely integral relationship between relaxation and performing well," says Mark Gittelman, M.D., F.A.C.S., a urologist and the director of the Miami Center for Sexual Health, who has also done clinical trials on Levitra. "That's why it's unfortunate that Viagra often has a whole ritual that goes along with it. Men can get tense at precisely the moment when they should be relaxing."

"As soon as you take it," Roger agrees, "you can't stop thinking about it." He compares it to missing a penalty kick in soccer—blow it once, and you'll be tense every time you take the field. During the 1-hour countdown until the Viagra tablet kicked in, Roger's performance anxiety kept growing. Making it worse was the fact that he knew that if it didn't work, Alyson would blame herself. No wonder his head started pounding.

Just when Roger's home life was at its bleakest, Dr. Holmes switched him to a remedy that didn't require any thought. "Cialis is attractive to people who don't like the notion of premeditated sex," says Dr. Holmes. Because Cialis can be taken just about anytime—on an empty or a full stomach, with a few beers or without—and is active for up to a day and a half, Roger could just pop a dose and forget about it. With only three pills a week, he could basically have it in his system all the time and perform whenever the mood struck, without any attendant anxiety—or debilitating headaches.

Within a week of filling his prescription, Roger had reversed years' worth of anxiety and inactivity. "I'm as good as new again," he says. Actually, even better—whenever he ships out with his fleet, he can leave the Cialis at home and not have to worry about suffering any unfulfilled oceangoing desires.

Alan Powell has no trouble kicking around the topic of his erection problems with strangers, though to this day he hasn't breathed a word about it to anyone in his family.

"That old taboo." He smiles grimly, sitting back in a chair under an uncomfortably detailed diagram of a penis hanging right above his head in Dr. Holmes's examining room. "I know it makes things worse, but I can't put it behind me." A 47-year-old general contractor from Hartlepool, in northern England, Alan looks a little Harry Potter-ish with his flopping hair and round glasses. And at 5'10", he keeps himself a lean 160 pounds by playing squash and soccer. Despite his age-defying face and overall fighting trim, however, Alan began to struggle to achieve erections when he was in his midthirties—sometimes succeeding, just as often failing.

Eventually, Alan's inability to either perform or explain destroyed his 14-year marriage. "My divorce was quite a blow to me, so when I finally met someone new, I was dead set on not making the same mistakes," he says. This time, he told his new girlfriend about his problem, and together they went to the urology clinic at St. Mary's Hospital.

Alan was momentarily relieved to discover there wasn't anything physically wrong with him. What he needed, said Louise Walker, C.U.N.P. (certified urologic nurse practitioner), was "a good kick start"—in other words, since his problem was psychological, he needed a chemical boost to get him past the performance anxiety and into a mindset in which he'd focus strictly on the sheer joy of gettin' busy. Alan started taking Viagra, which he found worked "about 75 percent of the time." He'd have gotten 100 percent out of it, he's convinced, if his girlfriend's situation had been less hectic. Because she was in the middle of her own divorce, they saw each other only a few nights a week.

"I wanted to impress her, and I knew these would be the only few hours we had," he says. "Mostly, the Viagra worked grand, but I had to wonder if the times it failed were because the window of opportunity shut too soon."

That's why, after conversations with Walker, long-lasting Cialis seemed like the answer. "My girlfriend was even more excited," Alan confides, darting his eyes momentarily at the half-open door of the examining room to see if any of the passing nurses can overhear. "She was getting all giggly, like she was a 16-year-old schoolgirl again." The results, however, were much better—and a little worse—than they'd expected. "It works bloody well—don't get me wrong," Alan says. "But it's been 2 days since I took the tablet, and I've still got this ache in my groin." It's not exactly an erection coming on, he says; it's more like a charley horse. But there's been no shortage of the right kind of response, either; even after an exhausting night and morning of sex, Alan found, he continued getting erections. "I'm sitting here watching the telly, trying to relax, and I feel one coming on again," he complains.

That can probably be fixed, says Dr. Murdock. Because the drugs are designed to treat men with serious vascular damage, a marginal case like Alan's might simply need a lower dosage. "Even these new drugs take some patient counseling," the doctor explains.

But Alan isn't ready to reduce his dosage of Cialis just yet. "Right now, I find that Viagra is more suitable if you know exactly when you're going to have sex," he concludes. "But if she's over for 2 days or we go on holiday together, I would take the Cialis and let what happens happen."

On the other hand, he still hasn't tried Levitra. . . .

The Jagodzinskis were having a great vacation on the English coast; so great, John cut a little looser than usual and tied on a bit of a load. That night, he couldn't get an erection. No big deal—had to be the booze. Then he failed the next day. He cut back on the pints. He failed again.

John couldn't understand it—sure, he's 53 years old, but at 6'1" and a taut 180 pounds, he's in better shape now than he was 20 years ago. Because he works the 5 P.M. to 11 P.M. shift as a bus depot inspector near his home in Portsmouth, his days are free for working out. He swims for an hour twice a week and runs the field, refereeing youth-league soccer games. "I'm quite healthy," says John. "Had my blood tests and prostate exam, and everything's in top form."

He waited months for his erections to spontaneously reappear, and when they didn't, he waited some more. In the meantime, his wife, Liz, had the same reaction as Alyson: She worried that John's body was a barometer of their relationship. "We didn't want the marriage to end over it, but it was putting a strain on us," she says.

Finally, nearly a year later, John broke through his embarrassment and went to St. Mary's. He was given a prescription for Viagra, but it took a little trial and error before he got the hang of it. "Any food at all, and it wouldn't have the right effect on me," John explains. Sometimes, he'd also get severely bloodshot eyes, which made him look "like an albino rabbit" and caused him a little embarrassment down at the bus depot. But taking only half a tablet at a time, he eventually discovered, gave him all the oomph he needed while reducing the rabbit-eye factor.

Still, after 10 months on Viagra, he was yearning for a little more spontaneity and went back to the clinic, this time taking home a prescription for Cialis. After trying it twice, however, John switched back to Viagra. "Cialis gave me a strange feeling of listlessness," he says. "It made my legs feel tired, and I got the bloodshot eyes again, but they lasted longer." Also, in his experience Viagra took effect nearly twice as fast, working in less than 20 minutes. "For me," he says, "Viagra is more responsive and controllable."

"Some men do report some muscle soreness and backaches from Cialis," says Dr. Holmes, probably because the drug inhibits not only PDE-5 but also another enzyme, which can cause muscle aches. This is the likely explanation for John's listlessness, as well. As for his red eyes, they're the result of increased bloodflow, though Viagra, and not Cialis, is usually the worse offender.

Of course, John could chop the Cialis pills down to manageable little fragments, but why bother when he can just go back to true blue? After all, Liz doesn't care. "As far as I can tell," she says, smiling, "we're right back where we used to be. They're both great in my eyes."

Back in Washington, D.C., Akhtar Qureshi is nightly going where few American men have gone before: into a bedroom that has Levitra on the night table.

Akhtar, 63, was one of those fortunate enough to have been selected to participate in a U.S. clinical trial of Levitra. His qualifications? More than a decade of impotence and a horrible reaction to Viagra.

Like Keith Henderson, Akhtar was ready to call it quits after diabetes ruined his sex life at age 50. At first, he tried going the holistic route. He hoped that flushing the excess sugar out of his blood would not only get his diabetes under control but also restore his lost erections. And while he shed 50 pounds, he ultimately came up short. "Even though I adjusted my diet and exercised, I still had ED," says Akhtar, the disappointment in his body's betrayal audible over the telephone.

At a loss, he then tried Viagra, but the side effects were miserable: Sometimes he'd get a jackhammer headache; other times, blurry vision and a stuffed nose. "Those are the kinds of problems you often have with Viagra," says Marc Shepard, M.D., who worked on the

Levitra trials. "Because it was the first of its kind, it's not as chemically selective as these latest-generation alternatives."

For 2 more years, Akhtar and his wife would occasionally revisit Viagra, but he so expected to feel lousy that he'd pretty much given up by the time the pill hit his belly. Akhtar's lucky break came when he was chosen to test Levitra.

On the new drug, Akhtar experienced none of the side effects of Viagra but all of the fun. Or at least it seems as if he had fun. "I took a tablet about 1 hour before, uh, intercourse, and then, uh . . . " Obviously, he's none too comfortable taking a stranger on a talking tour of his bedroom, and he struggles to find a delicate way to end the sentence. "The effects lasted long enough," he eventually stammers, "for me to complete my satisfactory sexual intercourse." Whew! But once he's gotten that out, he musters a little more nerve and really cuts loose—for Akhtar: "It was a very good experience!" he adds triumphantly.

Rubber Soul

We put our lives in their hands and our jimmies in their grip. They have brought more sex to more men than any cheap come-on, cologne, or aphrodisiac. They are condoms, and after reading this, you'll never wear them the same way again

BY MIKE ZIMMERMAN

JOE ENGLISH WON'T SHOW ME HIS NEW PENIS. Any other day, I would be grateful. But today I see 14 of his old ones standing tall on a wooden rack in his office, and I am disappointed. Each of these 15-inch monoliths—some studded, some swirled, some ribbed—is a testament to the creative engineering of a team assembled for one purpose: to build a better condom. The crystal-clear glass molds before me—mocking me, really, with their height—represent the current roster of players for Trojan, the nation's biggest rubber peddler. But what interests me most is the empty post at the end of the rack that, according to English, represents the future of the condom.

"We can't talk about that one," he says.

Of course. State secrets. But English, the manager of Trojan's manufacturing facility, does smile, as if he understands my need for answers. When it comes to rubbers, there's simply a lot we don't know—even though we've all used one at some happy point in our lives. Heck, thanks to AIDS, you could argue that Generations X and Y have used more rubbers than Generations A through W combined. According to a report from Johns Hopkins University, as many as 10 billion condoms are manufactured worldwide each year. Yet we slap them on our most valued body part without thinking about where

they come from or who they've been with or why we should trust
their ability to protect us. Condoms are our sexual partners as much
as any woman. Shouldn't we get to know them better before we take
them to bed?

As cultural artifacts, condoms tell us a lot about our collective
sex life—specifically, how it's changed from an unmentionable un-
dercurrent to a raging national torrent. Twenty years ago, if the words
"oral" and "anal" came up in a conversation, you were debating ther-
mometers. But now? We've gone from puritan to polymorphously
perverse in a generation. JFK was able to slip away and plonk Mafia
dolls in the shadows of the great national embarrassment, but
Clinton's hummer earned wraparound cable coverage and a vote in
the halls of Congress. A Supreme Court justice's confirmation hung
by a pubic hair; he was confirmed anyway. Cantaloupean breast implants, scrotal piercings, and college porn parties are part of the land-
scape. Yale, the alma mater of our last three presidents, now sponsors
an annual Sex Week, with lectures by pornographers. We talk dirty
during drive time, prime time, and Episcopal church conferences.
And we learned to speak freely because for a while there, our lives depended on it.

AIDS began a national debate about safe sex. It was the undis-
puted champion can opener when it came to wormy conversations.
The numbers tell us that we then took that conversation to the bedroom. According to the most recent National Center for Health Statistics survey, condom usage has risen nearly 70 percent since 1982.
The same conversations happened in high schools and Buick back-
seats, for in the same time frame condom usage by people having sex
for the first time tripled.

And you can see exactly why the rubber hit the road. Sex had
become simultaneously scarier and less hidden. Those little foil packs
are the equivalent of sexual Alka-Seltzer—calming upset libidos everywhere. You can't even use the things without imposing a reflective

pause on the action. You've got to stop, discuss, tear, deploy. It's like reviewing a call in the NFL: Caution tosses its flag on the mattress, and all eyes focus on the transgressor. And he's not allowed to play without his helmet on. "There's a lot more openness," says Michael Perry, Ph.D., a Southern California sex therapist and the founder of sexualintimacy.com. "There's a certain amount of paranoia driving it, which I don't like. But at least it's doing something to increase communication."

Perry also points to a more recent shift in our collective consciousness that he sees affecting condom usage. "People are sick of equating sex and death, so AIDS is off the radar. It's treatable. People who are HIV positive can lead normal, productive lives."

So, rather than the heavy baggage of disease prevention ("Buy, don't die" is not the most consumer-friendly marketing approach), the condom makers are coming around to pitch their products as the entrance ticket to the big sexual playhouse. That's why the most creative, provocative, and alluring condom designs have appeared only in the past few years. We're not scared anymore, so we need to be tempted.

Just outside of Princeton, New Jersey, nestled amid shade trees and cloistered inside an office complex that looks like a middle school, people are being paid to think about sex. More specifically, sex that sells. Ideas for new Trojan condom models come to fruition here in a very calculated swirl of ribs, studs, and, well, swirls. Words like "erection," "pleasure," and "lubricant" are thrown around this office the way "integrated business solutions" might be thrown around at IBM.

In a bare-bones conference room, the Trojan army awaits in perfect formation: two dozen boxes in a line down the length of the conference table, and at the far end, their generals, the R & D tag team of Richard Kline, vice president of marketing, and Michael Harrison, Ph.D., director of barrier-contraceptive development (a cooler title, I cannot imagine). Kline is 50-ish, graying, and cut cleaner than a Boy

Scout. Harrison is younger, equally well-groomed, tall, dark, and British—more Bond than Q, even though he spends his days in a lab. After they give me a quick tour of the products on the conference table, they treat me to the company line: The latex condom is a "medical device," and the company is not promoting sex, just safe sex.

Okay. But don't they spend their days dreaming up new ways to make "staying safe" a sheet-scorching experience? What's that like? "There are no real dark secrets," explains Kline. Ideas come out of informal meetings attended by about 10 employees, both "people in the business" and some from random areas of Amkel, Trojan's parent company. Ideas that meet certain "benchmark criteria"—that is, they include proven features like spermicidal lubricant, ribs, and so on—rise to the top of the list. Take Trojan's newest model, Twisted Pleasure. The design features a swirled, baggy head similar to the Inspiral condom (made by Intellx), a popular competitor that's been rated number one by several men's magazines. With that name, that shape, and a hot fluorescent-green box, how can Twisted lose? Less instantly likable—and salable—ideas fall to the bottom of the list. The Slim Fit design, for instance, died of the dual stigma of sounding uncomfortable and unflattering to the poor guy who needs one.

Harrison is the latex go-to guy. He's worked with Kline for 10 years, using his Ph.D. in polymer chemistry to ensure that any new idea can actually be built. "We've got 12 lab-based people who are committed to the research process," he says from across the conference table. "We make the prototypes to see if they'll hold the form, so to speak."

That form is a glass condom mold like the ones I saw in English's office. Harrison's team comes up with the design and sends the measurements to a glassblower, who in turn produces a batch of molds to be used for a limited production run.

Then comes the last, and biggest, hump: the road test. An out-

Fit to Be Tried

Condoms custom-tailored to a man's most personal measurements

Of the nearly 200 varieties of condoms available today, only eight feature any deviation in size—either a little larger or a little smaller. But Condomania has recently introduced They-Fit condoms, prophylactics custom-tailored to your penis size ($12 a dozen). "With condoms, size definitely matters," says Adam Glickman, president of Condomania.

The process is simple: Go to condomania.com and print out a "fit kit." Cut out the penis pattern and use it to measure your length and girth; then choose from 55 sizes (length goes from 3 inches to 10 inches, girth from "super-slim" to "extra-roomy"). Send your numbers through the secure Web site, and then wait for delivery. Are they worth it? "The difference is amazing," says our tester. "It slid on in a single stroke, and instead of anchoring itself with a pinching roll around base camp, it simply adhered to the entire shaft, second skin style. Once you've been custom-suited, an off-the-rack condom feels like punishment."

side firm recruits several hundred couples (both married and single), ages 18 to 34, willing to take the new condoms home and have at it anywhere from three to six times. Their ratings are compared with those of a control group of participants who've been rattling headboards with an established model. Understand: This is high-stakes fornicating, with millions of dollars hanging on hot sex. Consistently poor ratings in what Kline calls a "real-life use situation" are enough to pull the plug on the whole idea. He declines to divulge which condoms have crashed.

Not surprisingly, Harrison and Kline would rather celebrate the tester-approved designs arrayed before us. The three of us tear and unroll, and I feel the rumble strips of the Ultra Ribbed, the faux shark-skin of Pleasure Mesh, the subtle studs of Shared Sensation. Soon the table is littered with latex, and our fingers are dripping with lubricant. At which point Kline calls his assistant for a box of tissues. And I shake my head and smile. In any other Fortune 500 conference room, three guys ripping open rubbers and asking for tissues would be a movie of the week. Here at Trojan, it's just good business.

From Princeton I travel to Richmond, Virginia, where all Trojan con-doms are made. The factory is pure Wonka (with emphasis on the willies). There are the six "dip lines," essentially massive condom-making machines that churn through $2\frac{1}{2}$ tons of liquid latex every day. Each line is the size of a small apartment building—about 25 feet high, 15 feet wide, and, get this, almost a football field long (272 feet, to be exact). Within this framework is an endless conveyor of 7,000 glass molds passing up and down, back and forth, into and out of sight, completely self-contained and perpetual. It's the Trojan army, marching off to conquer a full 70 percent of the U.S. market.

The construction of a rubber goes like this: The clean mold dips into a moat of 70°F liquid latex—which looks and feels like skim milk left out for coffee—and is then baked at 240°F, dipped again, and baked again. With six dip lines popping condoms off the glass molds every second, that's more than half a million every day. More jimmy hats are created during my 2-hour tour than I could possibly use in a lifetime. Hell, more than your average NBA starting five could use in a lifetime.

Now the testing begins. If more than two condoms in every 1,000 fail, the entire production batch is tossed out. English won't give specific numbers, but he says it happens "so seldom that my blood pressure is okay." They pull condoms off the line at random and bring them to the "wet lab," where one group of techies fills condoms with water and manhandles them as another blows them up like party decorations. On my watch, they torture, mangle, and abuse at least a couple dozen condoms. Not a single one fails.

We head back out on the production floor so English can show me the shock testers—where every single condom goes on trial. Each conveyorlike machine has a perpetual line of upward-jutting phalluses. A pair of women slide the condoms over the mandrels, using a one-handed "whip 'n' flip" that would make a Chicken Ranch pro envious.

After the speed sheathing, the conveyor dips the mandrels into a small water trough. Two submerged electrodes zap the water (ouch!) and if the stainless steel inside the condom conducts any electricity, a signal tells the workers that the condom either is too thin or has a hole.

No failures on my watch. (Out in the field, the failure rate— mostly breaks and slips—is a scant 2.3 percent.)

Every condom that passes the ultimate test is rolled, fitted with a foil jacket, and treated to a quick glurt of lubricant, spermicide, or benzocaine (the anesthetic in the Extended Pleasure model that makes guys last longer.) All this spurting fluid makes me want to ask for a Wet-Nap.

Alas, the tour ends here—amid boxes piled high with packaged rubbers ready to be deployed. Again, the sheer numbers stagger me. A friend of mine who was in the navy during Vietnam once told me that when his ship would dock, a barrel of condoms would be waiting at the top of the gangplank for the sailors going on shore leave. They'd grab a handful and go. Well, I'm looking at enough condoms to fill 10,000 barrels. Our shore leave starts at the loading dock in this building, men. Line forms to the left.

And that's where they have us by the, well, you know. Condom manufacturers have come to understand the male psyche, and tap it. Guys like new toys. We like the impression that these toys are "advanced," whether it's a PDA or a prophylactic. We also like to please our women in bed—so we'll go for condoms called Twisted Pleasure that have just enough wink-wink kink to make them sexy, not scary, for the ladies. In fact, Kline notes that women are 35 percent of the market. Which is why the Her Pleasure model comes in a lilac-colored box. "Point being, we're never short of ideas," says Kline. "And if one of our ideas is copied by a competitor? That just means we've raised the entire category, and that's a good thing."

To which I reply: The men of America have got your rising category right here, Mr. Kline.

We live in an era in which the condom is no longer the token of shameful sex, or even deadly sex. That's probably a good thing. We've come to trust, and rely on, the sheath that shuts out rampaging microbes and shuts in impregnating sperm. It allows us to achieve a Zen-like focus on the delicious moment itself, without a thought for any consequences aside from our eventual gasp of pleasure, and maybe even hers. That's why I'm so interested in those hardworking R & D guys, the legions of dedicated home testers, and the people behind the marketing campaigns, selling the latest developments in strength and sensitivity. If they do their jobs right, they'll get right inside our imaginations, where the best part of sex takes place. And really, who among us couldn't use a little more Twisted Pleasure?

Joe English graciously sends me on my way with a handshake, a Trojan baseball cap, and a shopping bag full of freshly sealed samples. I leave well-stocked for years of both safe sex and party conversation. But of all the fascinating and absurd things I saw, there are two bigger lessons I've learned since I began my rubber odyssey. One, condoms freak people out. Leave a half dozen unrolled "reference condoms" on a paper towel on your office floor and people stop visiting. But I bet if everyone toured a condom factory, a naked rubber wouldn't be that big a deal. Perhaps this story can be your surrogate. I know that if you could see what I saw, you'd want to use more rubbers. Mostly because

Learn to Love 'em

Three tricks for turning condoms into sex toys

Even the smoothest seducer can be put off when it's time to put on a condom. To keep the ol' rip and unroll from redlighting a red-hot evening, try these strategies.

• **Mix and match.** Buy a half dozen boxes of various-colored and -textured condoms, separate them, and shuffle them in your night table drawer. The mystery condom then becomes part of the sexual anticipation. "What do we get tonight?" she asks. You reply, "Ribs, sweetie. I'll get the sauce!"

• **Talk it through.** A classic condom complaint: Putting it on brings action to a standstill. "Don't make it a big event," says Tracey Cox, author of *Supersex*. "Use the time to talk dirty to each other, rather than focusing on the job at hand."

• **Add a dab.** Place a dollop of lubricant on the head of the penis before putting the condom on, recommends Cox. Once it's on, swish and twist the condom around the entire head—"the lubricant inside makes it deliciously slippery," she promises.

they make you think about sex—but also because seeing them created makes you trust them more. I sure did.

And that fact leads to the second, and most important, thing I've learned. Condoms are not foolproof. See, my wife and I dug into that souvenir shopping bag. And we're now expecting our third child.

In Defense of Promiscuity

Macho doctrine says that sleeping with dozens of women
makes you a bigger man. But can it make you a better man?
A lothario presents his case   BY DANIEL ASA ROSE

Be not forgetful to entertain strangers:
for thereby some have entertained
angels unawares. —Hebrews 13:2

I HAD ALWAYS BEEN what's known as a one-woman man. But
after my divorce at age 30, I found myself pestilent, in the sense that
Blake meant it when he said, "He who desires but acts not, breeds
pestilence." I had desired for years and been constrained from acting
on my desires because of marital conventions and middle-class instinct. And those desires haunted me: Every time I saw a red mark on
a mirror, I thought it was someone's lip print. Every time I heard a
tomcat yowl, I thought the world was orgasming without me. And, as
many married folks know too well, it's only a few corrosive letters from
"regret" to "resent": I begrudged my wife for keeping me from the
party beyond. My brain was in my penis because both were starved.
It was going to take a lot of screwing around to separate them. But it
was also going to be the healthiest thing I could do.

Healthy? I heard the groans. Yes, I was aware of promiscuity's
bad press. My postdivorce yoga guru, among others, assured me that
my aspiration to make up for lost time was sordid. But to her I said
this: "You know what? I've been faithful to women in the past and

with any luck will be again in the future, but right now I am doing something else: meeting a lot of them fast, interacting with them fleetingly, parting from them cleanly. And in my hectic way, I try to honor them."

"Honor them?" she said. "By taking advantage?"

But this revealed the gaping misconception among those who have chosen to remain sexually cocooned. To me, the idea that I was taking advantage of anyone was patently prefeminist and patriarchal. Could my partners not say no? If during my sleepover stage I was fortunate enough to find women to have slumber parties with, it was only because they didn't want to sleep alone, either.

On the most basic level, my promiscuity was anesthetic: The application of hormones blocked the hurt. But beyond that, there was the salve of companionship. I turned to my sisters and they were there, opening their arms and hearts to me. I was agog at their generosity. What my guru couldn't grasp was that I treasured them for it, that my love for women deepened during this time of desperation, and that I had never found them more lovely and clever than I did then. For their part, I was always moved by how grateful they were for a bit of honest attention, how afterward they clamored to buy me breakfast or send me home with pot roast recipes to make for my sons. So eager were they, too, for the warmth of sexual friendship!

Let me hasten to say that I was not the world's greatest lover, by any stretch. I was passable. Sex was not a letter-graded enterprise, in any case—it always operated on the pass-fail system—but what made me a successful philanderer was that I was game. The one thing you can't fake to the opposite sex is interest. Plus this: Success begat success. It's a knack, like bicycle riding: Once you achieve that sense of balance, that foreknowledge that it is indeed possible to have a woman place your palm between her legs within 5 minutes of making her acquaintance, you're not likely to forget it. And, voilà, the confidence you bring to future encounters will be self-fulfilling.

Sordid? But surely you know it's closed spaces, not open ones, that breed fleas. It's the squirrelly gents in their IBM ties, casting furtive glances around the edges of the strip club, too nervous to come forward and tuck that bill where it needs to be tucked, who have the dirty minds. At the risk of sounding aphoristic, let me say that wild oats that are not sown tend to rot the pouch that holds them. Toss 'em with an open hand!

And at the risk of sounding like a proselytizer, might I also commend promiscuity for sheer melodrama? After all, no matter how good married sex might be, most monogamaniacs tend to roll over afterward and go to sleep. But denizens of the demimonde are privy to the suspense and danger of 2 A.M. Perhaps I'm in danger of romanticizing what was essentially the best education I ever got. I was doing a bunch of exotic travel writing in those days, and it was doubly edifying to learn the love habits as well as the local cuisine of a culture. With no language in common but sign language, I developed an almost animal kinship with those whose veins pulsed green beneath dusky skin, whose fingernails glowed orange-silver in the half-light of night kitchens. Meeting them in Scandinavian traffic jams and Arabian pet stores, I took instruction in the best sense of the word: making contact with the other side.

During those years, I also learned the answer to a grand question: Why does sleeping around cause some people to become what Saul Bellow has referred to as "f---ed out," while others become enlarged? It goes to the core of experience Blake was talking about. Why do some people come out of a Matisse exhibit rubbing their eyes with fatigue, while others come out exalted? In the course of my meanderings, I ran into an old college chum at a social in D.C. This woman had been a sexual renegade, scoring all my college friends before going on to bed most of the leading figures of the antiwar movement. By middle age, she should have looked haggard, spent of her precious life juices. But she looked radiant, living proof that at least in her case, the use-it-or-lose-it attitude trumped the notion that we had to carefully apportion our energies.

Yes, I had opened up. It was an exercise in enforced humanity, to attend to the triumphs and tragedies befalling my bedfellows. Women were willing to pool their woes with mine—and such woe to pool! I wept the night a nurse whose husband had abandoned her told how her 2-year-old daughter would climb into bed with her to rub her back the way she used to see her father do. "Mo, Mommy?" she would ask. "Mo?"

It was democratizing. I sampled a cross section of humanity I otherwise wouldn't have. I became unsqueamish, the way you do when you go to a square dance and relinquish the idea of washing your hands after each partner. Do-si-do—that's the fun of it! It reminded me of when I was first learning to drink as a 19-year-old studying theater in Dublin, and I was clambering down the stairs of a squalling pub behind a great drinking poet who had to clutch the brass rail for balance. Rather than seek to avoid his germs, I aimed to clutch where he did: We were all in this together! I was entering into the great animal condition the way a cat will roll in the warm morning sunshine for the sensual exuberance of it, for the festive purrability of it. So was I allowing myself to arch my back and be on the receiving end of a great gift: that of being a critter in the prime of life.

So I said yes, yes, a thousand times yes. Yes to the hotel hospitality hostesses of Haiti and the iambic interpreters of Iceland. Yes with her mismatched Disney socks, meeting me off the train in Machu Picchu. Yes with her saucy mouth and handcuff key ring, pouring my wine during an X-rated dinner in Auckland. Yes bandaging my middle finger in Addis Ababa, my poor middle finger I'd bent sideways after I dived into shallow water and was apparently in need of being nursed back to bed. Yes showing me how the hotel Murphy beds worked in Leningrad, after taking me out at 3 A.M. to watch the bridges open. Yes and yes to the hard-boiled Canadian

Mountie who said by way of inviting me into her bunk, "C'mon over and shake a paw." Yes and yes and yes, with apologies to Molly Bloom, who, if she were alive today, would no doubt welcome me on behalf of the Irish tourism council, beverage division.

But I've had enough of all that. Here is the unpestilent place I find myself in today: my groin and brain at a surgical remove from each other. I find myself able to sit in cafés with men, talking, without needing to check out each woman who passes. Or, if it's a woman I'm sitting with, to speak with her as she wants to be spoken with: as a human being rather than a female human being.

Once I phrased it this way, even my yoga guru eventually came around. She decided it was tantric—that I had achieved a desire-free state by acting on my desires, becoming free of lust through satisfying it. In other words, it was only because I had f---ed around with such dedication and industry that I could put the nonsense behind me. The redemptive power of promiscuity: the left-hand path to nirvana.

And now I'm able to be more attentive to my second wife than I ever was with my first because I've achieved a level of contentment, knowing that the energy I spent with her sisters was some of the most life affirming I've ever spent on this planet. I'm still curious, of course, but in an idle, noncompulsive way. The main thing I find myself wondering is where they are today, those fireflies of the past; if they are content; how they deal with getting older. And this, always: how many angels were in the mix. Because some surely were.

In Your Head
or in Your Pants?

A conversation with a professional surrogate

THINK PAYING FOR SEX IS A CRIME? Think again. While a dalliance with a prostitute may earn you a trip to county lockup, money-for-sex arrangements are still legal in much of America. The catch? You need a doctor's note.

Welcome to the world of sex surrogates (or, as the pros say, "professional surrogates"). Founded in the 1970s, the profession once boasted a workforce of 300 professionals dedicated to helping people in therapy overcome emotional and physical issues with intimacy by placing them in real-life sexual situations. Today there are far fewer sex surrogates, but they still exist. We went to Vena Blanchard, the president of the International Professional Surrogates Association, to answer a few questions about the practice, including one that pops to mind immediately: Is the emphasis of a surrogate's job the sex, or is it the therapy?

Who comes to see you?
Ninety percent are men. I'd say 50 percent of the clients are adults with an extreme lack of sexual and romantic experience. Another significant percentage of clients come to surrogate partner therapy because they're experiencing some kind of sexual dysfunction that is

preventing them from entering relationships: Inability to reach orgasm. Rapid ejaculation. Social anxiety.

There are also patients with emotional traumas: They've been victims of rape, incest, molestation, physical abuse as an extreme punishment, neglect, having a parent commit suicide, having a parent be mentally ill, having been tortured by all your peers for being a redheaded kid. Those things happening early in life leave the client traumatized and afraid of intimacy and closeness. In this type of therapy, clients can slowly, gradually move toward that emotional intimacy with the surrogate partner. This will trigger the client's issues. Then that allows the therapist and surrogate to help the client work through those issues so he or she is freer in future relationships.

What is critical to understand is that the vast majority of clients who come to this therapy are single. They don't have a partner.

In other words, they don't have someone who can help them get over these things?
Right. Most people work on these issues in the context of a loving relationship.

But why is a partner necessary? I imagine some people would argue that regular therapy should be enough.
Sexual concerns often are more effectively addressed in the context of a relationship. And many emotional difficulties are best addressed in the context of a relationship.

Some of the clients are unable to get into a relationship because of their difficulties, their shyness, or their body-image issues. Or, because they are ashamed about something else like a sexual dysfunction, they won't allow themselves to get into relationships.

How physically close do you become with someone?
It's not uncommon for people to imagine that this is about being sexual or having intercourse, rather than resolving sexual difficul-

ties. It's like saying the nature of a journalist's job is to hold a pencil. That may be part of what you do in the service of your job, but it's not the intent. It's a compassionate relationship. It isn't about the sex.

What happens during a session?
Surrogate and client and therapist make that determination in the context of each case. It is possible that the relationship would never progress beyond sitting and talking.

The beginning of the work involves talking and trust-building and relaxation exercises. The second stage is about the client getting more comfortable with his or her body, working through body image issues, becoming educated through reading and through conversations with therapist and surrogate about sexuality and about emotional relationships. At the same time, the touching becomes more sensual: hands, face, feet, the back side of the body. It's not traditionally sexual, but it's a chance for the client to become more comfortable in his or her own body and, at the same time, develop the relationship with the surrogate partner. In this process, the client's difficulties with physical and emotional intimacy emerge. Then the therapist and surrogate and client get to work those through.

Sometimes the work progresses to a stage of touching genitals and what might be considered traditional sexual touch. If it goes there, it's because the client has issues that can't be resolved without doing that work.

So, this isn't something where you slide right into bed. . . .
This is a gradual process. It's not prostitution. It's not even sexual enhancement for the sexually bored. It's really therapy.

For the people who need it, if they don't get a sense that it's safe and gentle, then they'll be too afraid. Knowing that there's a therapist involved helps some of the people who imagine that they can just call somebody off the Internet and pursue this. There are people who advertise "surrogate" work. I found one Web site that offered "dual surrogate oil massage." That's not surrogate work. It's using the word "surrogate" in order to camouflage prostitution.

Do people sometimes worry themselves and overthink themselves into these dysfunctions?
Yes. Absolutely. Guys have feelings. The problem is that they think they're not supposed to. They may be mad at themselves for having emotional as well as physical needs. And so a big part of all therapy, including sex therapy and surrogate partner therapy, is helping people to know themselves and accept themselves and to feel good about expressing themselves to others.

A common myth is that it's about technique, and it's really about how to be aware of yourself and express yourself and accept yourself. And those things happen to, paradoxically, make you a better lover.

How can we get ourselves out of this trap? Should we just stop thinking and just do it?
Try it. Ideally, sexuality is a vacation from all that overthinking and worry. A loving relationship is a vacation from the social mask and the requirement to be vigilant and self-protective. A good relationship is like coming home and relaxing.

There's a price we pay for the protection. Some of our clients in this therapy were so wounded in early life relationships that they determined to protect themselves and have not been able to allow themselves the closeness that they now long for, which would have helped them grow up and mature and build emotional strength. Now they feel young and afraid; only they're in grown-up bodies, and they feel embarrassed about their lack of experience and their fear.

How do you help clients past superficial images, body-image issues?
If I had the answer to that, my life would be so much easier. That takes time. The therapist and the surrogate work together to help the client beyond superficiality in general, to pay attention to the person who lives inside their body and inside their partner's body and not just focus on the body. I had this wonderful, funny, intelligent man who was extremely overweight and terrified to even ask someone for a date because of his weight, and so humiliated with his weight that he refused to take his clothes off with anyone. And in truth, in this culture, his appearance kept many people from appreciating him as a romantic partner. But he was even more rejecting than the rest of the world.

The whole world needs therapy.
Probably. But there must be a few people who aren't superficial. Actually, I think a lot of people aren't superficial, and you have to find them and be willing to leave your house. This man was not willing to leave his house because of his body-image issues. Then there are the other clients, who are overly focused on what the partner's body looks like and have lost the rest of their senses: sounds and sensations and smells. They've shut off all their senses but their eyes.

Where could someone find a surrogate?
There are surrogates in Australia and Israel and California, but there really are a limited number of surrogates, and they're difficult to locate. There are fewer than 100 surrogates in the country. One of the best ways to find a surrogate is to contact the International Professional Surrogates Association, www.surrogatepartner.com.

Why in California, and not in, say, Washington or Florida?
There are surrogates in Florida. Back in the 1970s, when therapists were first discovering sex therapy and surrogate partner therapy, there were a number of therapists in California who wanted to establish the

legitimacy of surrogate partner therapy. They put on a conference at UCLA, in the mid-1970s, attended by legislators, attorneys, surrogates, therapists. In conversation with the state, they established that surrogate partner therapy could operate legitimately in the state of California, so there are fewer questions about the legality of the work. The truth is that there are no laws prohibiting surrogate partner therapy anywhere in the United States. But anxiety based on a misunderstanding of what the work is inhibited therapists from being comfortable referring to surrogates in some other locations. And there just aren't a lot of surrogates left.

There used to be several hundred. Now there are between 50 and 100 in this country, maximum. There are more self-help books. Managed care and the changes in health insurance have reduced the payments for psychotherapy; fewer people are getting to psychotherapy, and they are not staying in psychotherapy to do more than crisis management. Fewer people are referred to surrogate therapy. It's an expensive process if you have to pay both the therapist and the surrogate out of pocket, and these days that's more the case than it used to be.

Insurance won't cover this?

Insurance has never paid for surrogate partners because they're not licensed. But it used to pay for psychotherapy that the client would have with the therapist, and it pays less and less for fewer and fewer things, with fewer sessions. Since people misunderstand what the work is and imagine it's just engaging in sex, and since anxieties about HIV and STDs in general have reduced the number of people who are willing to refer surrogates, the number of people willing to train as surrogates and the number of clients who are comfortable with the idea have gone down. There remain many more clients who need this therapy than there are surrogates and local therapists able to work with them.

QUICKIES

SHAVE YEARS ONTO YOUR LIFE

Researchers in the United Kingdom have found that men who shave their faces daily have sex more often than guys who shave less frequently. Even more impressive: Daily shavers are up to 24 percent less likely to die of a stroke than their less hairy counterparts, who don't need to shave as frequently. But don't invest in Gillette just yet. Researchers attribute the findings to lifestyle differences and hormone levels, not the act of shaving itself.

SEXUAL HEALING

As good as a daily aspirin is for heart health, daily sex may be even better (and no childproof cap!). A recent study shows the more sex a man has with a woman, the better his cardiovascular function. When German researchers asked 120 adults to monitor the frequency of various sexual acts, they found that the men who had the most intercourse also had the best heart rate variability. "Greater heart rate variability is associated with better cardiovascular function and lower mortality in various studies," says Stuart Brody, Ph.D., the study author. Vaginal intercourse, rather than other types of sex, may have the greatest cardiac benefit because of an evolutionary imperative to reward reproductive behavior, says Brody.

A CLUE THAT SHE'S ON THE PILL

If you're a certain kind of man, there's a certain kind of woman who's looking for you. In a series of trials, Scottish researchers found that women taking birth control pills have different tastes in men than women who aren't on the Pill. The studies suggest that women on birth control pills were more attracted to men with rugged, manly features, such as strong, wide jaws and big cheekbones, while women not taking the Pill preferred men with softer, more feminine features. The reason appears to be a shift in hormone levels caused by the Pill, say the researchers.

SEX IN THE CITIES

There's probably a woman out there who finds copious ear hair "cute." But aural sex fetishes aside, women aren't usually alone in what turns them on about men. In fact, data from the online dating service Match.com shows that at least some ladies who get hot and bothered (or just bothered) by particular male traits are concentrated in the same zip codes. Check out this city sampler.

SAN FRANCISCO: Turned on most by Ph.D.s

DENVER: Turned on most by men with long hair

DETROIT: Turned off most by regular drinkers

MIAMI: Turned off most by men with a few extra pounds

PORTLAND: Turned on most by nondrinkers

PITTSBURGH: Turned on most by men with tattoos

AUSTIN: Turned on most by men with red hair

CHICAGO: Turned off most by long hair

ROSE TO THE OCCASION

Men know flowers like women know brake fluid. That's why we're offering these bouquet-giving tips—so you don't put the wrong kind in her hands.

Situation: First date

BEST FLOWER: Sunflowers

WHY: They're informal, so she won't feel as if you're putting a lot of pressure on her. Send them the morning after the first date.

Situation: A trip makes you miss something important, like her birthday

BEST FLOWER: Orchid plant

WHY: Women generally view long-lasting plants as thoughtful, which makes them a good comeback when she thinks you're not.

Situation: A milestone birthday or anniversary

BEST FLOWER: Vase of Casablanca lilies

WHY: Women like them because they're one of the world's most impressive-looking flowers. *Tip:* Use a tissue to remove the rust-colored pistils; they'll stain your shirt or her dress.

Situation: After the fight

BEST FLOWER: Anything but carnations

WHY: They're cheap, which is exactly the way you'll look if you try to make amends with these.

Situation: Secretary's Day

BEST FLOWER: Potted African violet

WHY: A neutral plant expresses gratitude and accents her desk. Avoid roses, which roughly translate to "I want you right now, on the desk."

Situation: You pop the question

BEST FLOWER: Red and white roses

WHY: She—and all of her friends—will admire the symbolism. Red for love, white for eternity. Just like a Budweiser can.

A Delicate Groom

I know today's women want men with cool haircuts, clean nails, and fashionable clothes, but do you also expect us to trim our pubic hair? —M.B., VIA E-MAIL

Unless it looks as if Gene Shalit has started broadcasting movie reviews from between your legs, there's no need to mess with your gorilla salad (which, disturbingly, is how one of my friends refers to his below-the-belt pelt).

Women expect guys to be pretty hairy down there, and we don't mind it at all. On the other hand, if it does look as if our favorite *Today* show critic has moved into your pants, take a pair of sharp scissors (careful, now) and begin trimming ¼ inch at a time—reducing the length but being careful to keep it uniform—until it looks lush but not overgrown. Don't shave or cut too close, or you'll look as if you work part-time making porn, which, from a woman's point of view, would not be a good thing.

Bare Down There

Do you see this Brazilian bikini wax trend lasting? I like the natural look. —MARC, NEW YORK CITY

The craze is waning, thank goodness. It was a painful, pointless trend that left women feeling frumpy if we had more than a guitar-pick-size patch of hair down there. Several of my fashion-forward friends say they now favor trimming off a little at the edges for neatness but leaving the rest alone. That sounds good—natural and low mainte-nance. But who can predict? Such is the nature of pointless trends.

Pay Date

If she suggests the date, does that mean she plans to pay?

—D.D., MIAMI

Probably not. Regardless of who did the inviting, most women expect you to pick up the tab on the first date. When in doubt, leave the check on the table. If she snatches it up and insists on paying, thank her and promise to treat next time.

If she suggests splitting it, insist on paying the whole thing, giving in only if she protests adamantly. Check still there after 10 minutes? She doesn't care or is waiting for you to pony up. So pony up.

Taking a Shine

What's the deal with lip gloss? My wife puts it on so much, it's like she's addicted to it.   —DAVE, GAINESVILLE, FLORIDA

First reason: the ubiquitous advertising that assures women that natural, lip-colored lips are completely undesirable. Cosmetics ads imply that a truly gorgeous mouth should have the tint and luster of a freshly waxed sports car, not a human body part. Second, the stuff she's using to moisten her kisser may actually cause her mouth to feel drier and tighter as it evaporates, prompting her to reapply. Last, she may lick her lips because of the flavor or stickiness of the gloss. The more she licks, the drier her lips become, prompting her to reapply. Now you know. This information won't make her stop, but maybe it will help you tolerate her mostly harmless habit.

THE MYSTERIES OF WOMEN

Understanding girls is easy. Girls like to play Make-Believe. They like to giggle. They like riding pink bicycles and dressing up in mom's clothing.

But you're not trying to understand girls. You want to know about women—creatures who are far more complicated (and far less likely to dress in mom's clothes). And that, my friend, is something most men will never do.

But you aren't most men—you're inquisitive (after all, you're reading this book) and you're prepared to do the legwork it takes to solve the mysteries of women. Keep reading and you'll uncover a bevy of clues that will get you to your goal in no time.

The 25 Sexiest Things Ever Said by Women

In the battle of he said, she said, you know who always gets the last word

COMPILED BY AMY JO VAN BODEGRAVEN

1. The serpent beguiled me, and I did eat. –EVE, GENESIS 3:13

2. To err is human—but it feels divine. –MAE WEST

3. We're so damn conservative all day that when you finally get us in the bedroom, we're absolute animals.
–SHANNEN DOHERTY, ON BEING REPUBLICAN

4. Lust is the sin that gets me excited. Luckily, because I'm married, I also get good jewelry out of it. –HEATHER LOCKLEAR

5. All I can say is if they show my butt in a movie, it better be a wide shot. –JENNIFER LOPEZ

6. I don't think I have to introduce myself, unless you don't recognize me with my clothes on. –MADONNA

7. If you want to turn on your boyfriend, get naked and strap on an accordion. –SHERYL CROW

8. It says "Pamela." And when he gets excited, it says "I love Pamela very, very much. She's a wonderful wife, and I enjoy her company to the 10th degree!" –PAMELA ANDERSON, ON THE TATTOO ON TOMMY LEE'S PENIS

9. Most virtue is a demand for greater seduction.
–NATALIE CLIFFORD BARNEY

10. Only the united beat of sex and heart can create ecstasy. –ANAÏS NIN

11. It's pitch, sex is. Once you touch it, it clings to you.
–MARGERY ALLINGHAM

12. As a stripper, I was getting a taste of what it would be like to be a woman in a society that honors the animal vitality in us all, instead of despising it. —SEPH WEENE

13. It was like experiencing a nuclear explosion in a very small place. —LONI ANDERSON, DESCRIBING SEX WITH *WKRP IN CINCINNATI* COSTAR GARY SANDY

14. I get such a rush going to the store, standing in front of the condom counter and going through them. I love the gold-coin ones. Every time I undo one, it reminds me of the chocolate candies from my childhood. —SANDRA BULLOCK

15. I don't think being obsessed with sex is any stranger than being obsessed with stamp collecting. —ANNIE SPRINKLE

16. I'm very old-fashioned. Occasionally I do wear underwear. —SHARON STONE

17. Men ought to become more conscious of their bodies as objects of delight. —GERMAINE GREER

18. A kiss is a lovely trick designed by nature to stop speech when words become superfluous. —INGRID BERGMAN

19. You wanna know what my tongue feels like? —JANET JACKSON

20. You see a lot of smart guys with dumb women, but you hardly ever see a smart woman with a dumb guy. —ERICA JONG

21. Don't! Ever! Stop! F---ing! Me! —KELLY PRESTON, IN *JERRY MAGUIRE*

22. Is she perverted like me? Would she go down on you in a theater? —ALANIS MORISSETTE

23. I'm not a prostitute, but I could give you what you want. —MISSY ELLIOTT

24. When she raises her eyelids, it's as if she were taking off all her clothes. —COLETTE

25. I like to wake up feeling a new man. —JEAN HARLOW

How Women Work

Understanding their quirks will make for a more perfect union

BY BRUCE JAY FRIEDMAN

I**NNUMERABLE ATTEMPTS HAVE BEEN** made to unravel the mystery of female behavior. All have ended in failure.

"What does woman want?" the great Freud asked in frustration. He went to his grave without an answer. Novelist John Updike might have come as close to the truth as anyone. Above all else, he suggested, women want to dance.

You have as much chance of deciphering a woman's thought process as you would of solving Fermat's Last Theorem. Or even his Next-to-Last Theorem.

Here are six mystifying quirks of female behavior that make the fair—and often unfair—sex both maddening and irresistible.

THEY DON'T DEAL

A handshake with a man is a sacred covenant, to be broken only on pain of death or serious injury. It's an agreement you can take to the bank—unless, of course, you're dealing with a Hollywood producer. Shake hands with a woman, however, and you do so at your own risk. Too often, the result is a deal-ette.

DAN: How come you're not packed? You agreed that we were going to move back to my hometown in Minnesota.

NAN: And freeze my ass off? Are you crazy?

DAN: We had a deal. We shook hands on it.

NAN: I meant it at the time.

SECRET? SCHMECRET

Entrust a secret to a male friend and—once again, unless he's a Hollywood producer—the chances are it will go no further. Share that same confidence with a woman and you might as well broadcast it on CNN.

DAN: When I told you about Bill's affair with his hairstylist, you promised to keep it a secret. Now everyone in town knows about it, and his wife just left him.

NAN: The only one I told was Linda.

DAN: But she told six other people.

NAN: Is it my fault she can't keep a secret?

THEY NEVER FORGET

Despite their vaunted reputation, elephants do occasionally forget something—an old bag of peanuts, a trainer they might have eaten. This is not the case with women. They forget nothing.

NAN (*annoyed*): How come you told me that my girlfriend Judy is hot?

DAN: When did I say that?

NAN: In Mexico. We were sitting around the pool. She was wearing a striped bikini.

DAN: But that was 7 months ago.

NAN: Well, do you still think she's hot?

OR MAKE MISTAKES

Women are constitutionally unable to admit to a mistake—even at the point of a gun. It's probably some kind of genetic malfunction. The last time a woman admitted to a mistake was during the Byzantine Empire in 14th-century Constantinople. The woman in question, Fatima Abdullah, later recanted and said it was a mistake to admit she'd made a mistake.

DAN: How could you have gotten us into DumbTech? We bought it at $60 a share, and it's now down to 12 cents.

NAN: One of these days, that stock will go through the roof. Your problem is that you don't think long term.

THEY DESPISE THEIR BODIES

There are men who are short, fat, and losing much of their hair—and they still have a high opinion of themselves. This is not the case with women. Outwardly vain, even the most spectacularly attractive member of the species feels that somehow, appearance-wise, she hasn't made the grade.

DAN (*lustfully admiring Nan's perfectly shaped body as she stands before a mirror*): You look fabulous.

NAN: How can you say that? What about my thighs?

THEY SNORE, YOU KNOW

Call it a crime against nature, but a surprising number of women snore. Even otherwise flawless types, not just butterballs. But no woman will ever admit to it.

DAN (*haggard from lack of sleep*): Boy, you really raised the rafters last night. I didn't get 10 minutes of sleep.

NAN: How many times do I have to tell you? I don't snore.

DAN: I've got proof now. This time I recorded it. Listen to this. (*takes out cassette player*)

NAN (*after listening*): That's not me. I can't believe you taped yourself snoring.

Just Be a Man

6 simple suggestions. Really simple

BY AMY SOHN

WHAT I WANT IN A MAN IS A MAN. After 10 years of dating scrubs, pushovers, and narcissistic artists, I recently fell in love with a guy named Jake. When I tried to figure out how Jake was different from the others, I realized it all came down to one thing: He's a man. And a man is not the same as a boy. Not even close.

Jake showers before coming over, listens to me when I talk, and doesn't have a conniption when he tries to say, "I love you." We don't have huge screaming arguments over his ability to commit. Instead, we eat candlelit dinners, argue about movies, and make stupid fart jokes.

If you, like most men, want to be a man but suspect that you're a hybrid, a Boy with Man Rising, here are a few basic steps to help with the transition. Think of them as an automatic bar mitzvah.

1. A MAN GOES DOWN. No excuses. No hesitation. Don't wait to be asked; offer. Don't do it for 2 minutes and then resurface happily, expecting some sort of trophy for participation. Stoop to conquer and you will. Don't complain about hair, smell, consistency. If there's a problem down there, you're allowed to have second thoughts about the girl, but in general keep your mouth shut.

Be willing to stay there about as long as your favorite sitcom lasts, and possibly longer. If she taps your shoulder and says, "It's okay—you can come up," respond with "Is there anything I could be doing better?" because she doesn't really mean "It's okay—you can come up." She means "You need to move to the left" or "Try the Japanese alphabet, not the English." Half the tappers out there just don't believe you want to be down under, so the best way to convince them you're for real is to refuse the tap. It may take some discipline, but remember: You will be rewarded.

2. A MAN KNOWS HE IS NOT THE ONLY MEMBER OF THE RELATIONSHIP WHO HAS A CAREER. As "nesty" as women may be, when we enter relationships, we can feel conflicted, too. We worry that we're not spending enough time with our friends, our work, our family, and, believe it or not, ourselves. So when a man goes on and on about his job and how demanding it is, he comes off as a self-centered jerk, unless he's Ari Fleischer. So the next time you hear yourself saying "I really need to focus on my work right now," to explain where you're coming from or to get out of the relationship, do the girl a favor and dump her so she can find somebody else.

3. A MAN IS CURIOUS. Women are trained to ask questions and listen. That's what we do with our girlfriends. It doesn't mean we always want to be listening to you the whole time, though. I once dated a guy who went on about his job for the entire length of a 5-hour car ride, without ever asking me about what I do, which is write a column about sex—not exactly a conversation stopper. That was our last date.

4. A MAN FEELS. I once had a man tell me, a few months into our relationship, that he felt as if I'd been pushing him away. I immediately burst into tears—not out of guilt but from gratitude. The fact that he could voice such a complaint was proof to me not only that he cared but that he cared enough to communicate.

A little goes a long way. So many men have a hard time expressing their feelings about anything, from the taste of their blackened salmon to the reason they cried at *Frequency*, that we're overjoyed just to hear them say something as simple as "I feel close to you right now."

5. A MAN BENDS. Maybe because like attracts like, I've dated more than my share of sticks-in-the-mud—and paid the price. I once told a boyfriend I felt he had been patronizing me in public, and he said, "I wasn't! I have a novelist's eye for detail, and I can tell you I wasn't!" What made me mad wasn't that he disagreed with my interpretation but that he seemed to think I was objectively, qualitatively incorrect. People are never incorrect when they say what they feel.

When you find yourself in one of those fights where, as Bob Dylan put it, "everything I'm saying, you can say it just as good," try to bend a little. Tell her you can see how she might feel a certain way, even if you didn't intend for her to. Women appreciate it when you give them the benefit of the doubt.

That's it. Take these reminders out into the bars and restaurants and streets, and women will be putty in your manly hands. But before you do, destroy this so your future girlfriend doesn't find it, because the most important rule of manhood is . . .

6. A MAN MAKES MANHOOD LOOK EASY.

The Vagina Dialogues

**Ever wonder what women really say when they talk about men?
So did we**

MODERATED BY HEATHER BUCHANAN

THERE'S A FANTASY etched as clearly into the male imagination as that picture of dogs playing poker. It concerns an unknown bar—or, better still, a secret suite in a Manhattan hotel—where smart and beautiful women gather to drink chardonnay and discuss the manipulation of the male libido in terms that would make David Mamet blush. The hour grows late. The wine flows some more. There is a ritual incantation loosely based on the Spice Girls' early writings. The Twister board comes out. The lights dim, and . . .

Few men besides eunuchs, hairstylists, and David Doyle (when he played Bosley on the original *Charlie's Angels*) have ever breached this door that separates the sexes. Until now, that is. For what follows is the real story—not the rules, not the clichés, but the truth as best we know it about what women really want.

THE PANEL

Like participants in a totally hot witness protection program, these spirited and candid ladies were happy to talk dirty to us but requested that their last names be withheld.

CHERYL. Single mom. A tall, blue-eyed beauty from the Midwest who, when she's not at work as a political coordinator, likes to hula hoop and to ride horses bareback. She has a giving personality and is the friend you would call in a crisis.

DEBORAH. Single. A spa owner who would like to have a husband and a family someday. She dates often but still hasn't met the right guy.

HEATHER. Divorced. Formerly married to a Los Angeles screenwriter, this sex columnist started writing as a way to work through issues that arose during her breakup. She uses humor as a way to cope with pain.

ILANA. Married and pregnant. As an actress, she intuitively understands how role-playing and improvisation can keep a relationship fresh. But also as an actress, she's acutely aware that youth and beauty are fleeting. Her husband is an actor, as well.

NANCY A. Lives with her boyfriend. A soulful rock 'n' roll singer who's in it for the joy rather than the cash. Her favorite pair of cowboy boots is 20 years old, and she's a champion at shucking oysters.

NANCY M. Single. This sexy architect possesses the steel necessary to deal with New York real estate developers, but it's tempered with old-fashioned femininity.

SHANNON. Single. Still in her twenties, this broadcast producer is sassy and open to new experiences. Marriage isn't first and foremost in her mind.

Why don't we start with this: What qualities make a man attractive?
Ilana: Hot sex isn't enough anymore. It can't be all passion and no stability. We might stay in a relationship longer than we should because we're tied in to his looks—like this one Brad Pitt look-alike boyfriend I had—but it doesn't last.

Heather: I used to be attracted to the AA guy—Asshole Appeal. Now, even though he's still around and kind of cute, it doesn't work. Compassion is key. Be nice to me, be nice to my incontinent bichon frise, and I'm yours. I fell in love with a man I dated because he was so kind to my father, who suffered from Parkinson's disease. The time and effort men put in with my friends, family, and pets pay off in spades.

Cheryl: It sounds like a cliché, but I truly want a man who is a good communicator. Between a vibrator and a sperm donor, I can do the rest myself.

Nancy M.: I look for a guy who has passion and drive: a drive to have fun, a drive to be responsible, a drive to make a legacy for himself. Someone who gets the big picture and wants to leave this world a better place when he's done with it. It's almost Darwinian—finding a good provider and father.

Deborah: I think a guy who talks about what it means to be a dad, with the kids he either has or would like to have, is a total turn-on. A man has to be clear about his agenda. If he doesn't want kids, he should say so. It's not fair to waste a woman's fertile years.

Dating is certainly more complicated when you're not in your twenties anymore. What do you think about being involved with a man who's older—say, over 40?

Nancy A.: Forty is the new 30.

Nancy M.: It's better if they've sown their wild oats.

Heather: As they get older, they're more concerned with my orgasm, instead of just their own.

Cheryl: A guy over 40 who's never had a serious relationship is a red flag. If he was married before or engaged, or at least in a long-term relationship, it shows his ability to commit. If not, I'd really have to wonder about the guy.

Should all of his exes live in Texas?

Ilana: A guy who trashes his ex is totally unattractive. When the relationship is new, keep the chatter down about the ex. Until I know where I am in his life, I don't want to know where she is.

Heather: I know a guy whose ex-wife came up as "F---ing Bitch" on his cell phone caller ID. That's a signal that I could be "F---ing Bitch Number Two."

Nancy M.: Leave old baggage out of the new relationship. Don't hold the present lover accountable for the sins of the past lover.

So what's a turnoff in a guy?

Ilana: Trying a new move, then telling you, "Well, everyone else really liked it."

Nancy A.: Yelling at waiters or waitresses. Every girl has either been a waitress or been friends with one at some point in her life. If the waitress has dropped hot soup in his lap, he can knock himself out, but if she's forgotten to bring the water and he's turning red, I'm gone.

Nancy M.: Judgmental men and negativity are turnoffs. My last boyfriend had a negative comment to say about everybody, from friends to people in the news. To him, everyone was an idiot. It really brought me down.

Cheryl: Nose hair. It's superficial but important. Invest in a trimmer.

What's a turn-on in a guy?

Nancy A.: Confidence.

Deborah: Taking his time.

Make a Brilliant Save

When your wife or girlfriend catches you staring at another woman, keep staring. Stare as if you're catatonic, and respond only when she pokes you in the shoulder three times. Act startled—as if you've been awakened from a daydream—and say, "You know, I was just thinking about that wonderful weekend in the Poconos, and how much fun we had in that heart-shaped bathtub." Just like that, you'll be off the hook.

Cheryl: I'd say 360-thread-count sheets. He's not in college any-more. Make the bed a place I can't wait to lie down and get naked in. It also doesn't hurt to talk dirty.

Heather: I can literally be talked into an orgasm.

Shannon: Yeah, but not if he's describing you like an eighth-grade textbook.

Nancy M.: A turn-on is someone who kisses well and who oozes an appetite for sex. Someone who knows the difference between screwing and making love . . . and does both.

Nancy A.: It really depends on my desire for him. I know two guys who kissed the same way—one revolted me, and the other made my knickers wet. If I really fancy him, he will most likely be an excellent lay.

Ilana: Men who compliment your body during sex are won-derful. I love it when my guy says, "You look so sexy pregnant." Don't stop viewing a woman sexually when she becomes a mother.

What makes a man great in bed?

Shannon: Any man can be good in bed, but being great in bed is hard to achieve. Any man who gives more than he takes, especially in the beginning, is A-OK with me. Foreplay is exactly what it sounds like—you have to warm up before you can play a good game.

Nancy A.: Tell me what feels good. I'm not a mind reader. Feed-back is good. When I'm doing something that feels terrific, tell me. I'll put it on speed dial.

Heather: I love it when he's just shaved before he rubs his cheek on my inner thigh. It's like smooth against smooth.

Shannon: I want a guy who can find the turtle in the giggle patch.

Cheryl: Where the hell did that come from?

Shannon: My mother.

Nancy M.: What on earth is a turtle in a giggle patch?

Shannon: It's the clitoris, you ninny.

Heather: But seriously, with something like finding the G-spot, *I* don't even know where that is. How's *he* supposed to find it?

Ilana: There's a lot of literature out there, from the *Kama Sutra* to Kim Cattrall's orgasm book. He can read, right?

When you've been in a long-term relationship and things are getting routine, how do you keep the spark alive?

Heather: Familiarity breeds routine. Get out of your comfort zone and your routine and your bedroom. There is no such thing as bad sex in a hotel. I went out with a guy for 2 years before we had sex in his pickup truck. It might have saved the relationship if we'd tried it sooner.

Shannon: Yeah, oral sex in the coatroom of your favorite restaurant or the bathroom at your relatives' house on Thanksgiving. Come on, it's only 15 minutes, and if it's great, you can shave it down to 5.

Cheryl: Variety, variety, variety. Of course, it doesn't work with the jealous types because they'll just wonder where you learned the new trick. Variety can come in the form of clothing (role-playing every once in a while) or a new hair color or style, or just doing something you know he likes that doesn't happen very often. But it must come from him, too.

Shannon: Porno tapes. Pornography works wonders. I'll be in the shop, and I'll call to tell him, "I'm buying Seymour Butts's latest video." He'll remind me that they tape all his calls at work and maybe we should talk about it later.

Ilana: Tell us your fantasies. If we love you, we'll do anything . . . then ask us what we want.

Heather: Right on. If he does what she wants, he gets the power back. It's like that "pay it forward" thing. Worship your woman, and she'll worship you back.

Cheryl: Worship, wow! That's a beautiful word, "worship."

All: Amen!

QUICKIES

Fightin' Words

Trying to win an argument with a woman? Here's a hint: Stop.

"Winning an argument is an oxymoron for most couples," says Patricia Love, Ed.D., a relationship consultant and author of *The Truth about Love*. "You'll rarely get the last word with a woman, but even if you do, it doesn't mean anything if you haven't resolved the problem."

What does she want? To know you're listening and understanding her point of view—which is what you want from her, too. So when you start overheating, try Love's 2-minute drill: Let your wife talk for 2 minutes while you listen. Now it's your turn. "You'll keep it succinct and get to the point, with no interruptions," Love says. After a few of these serve-and-volleys, she'll know you're listening, and you'll be closer to resolving your problem. Now, slap hands and shower up.

Do You Know What She's Thinking?

It's challenge enough to notice when a woman has a new hairstyle, let alone get inside her head. So we asked some experts what she's day-dreaming about, and we're mightily thrilled. "Women can have an orgasm from fantasy alone," says sex researcher Beverly Whipple, Ph.D., just to get our attention. "Women are more pleasure-oriented than goal-oriented about sex." Acting out her fantasies—to a point—can bring out her inner vixen. Like this:

Invite Friends
Women commonly think about a threesome or group sex, but few truly want to do it. So use the power of suggestion, says Ava Cadell, Ph.D., Ed.D., a sex therapist and the author of *12 Steps to Everlasting*

Love. Her idea: Heat things up by pretending someone else is in the room and asking what she'd like that person to do to her. Or initiate some PG-13 action in an elevator and talk about what you think the security camera is seeing.

Be Tough
"Women often fantasize about a forced sexual encounter," says Candida Royalle, president of the adult film company Femme Productions. Don't overdo it, but showing her who's boss can relieve her of responsibility and some of the guilt women associate with sex, Royalle says. It can be as simple as carrying her to bed or tackling her when she walks in the door.

Attach Strings
"Women often want to be restrained, which is also scary for them," says Whipple. You have to be careful to walk the line between exciting fear and real fear, so use something gentle, like a scarf.

Play Pretty Woman
You have fantasies about Julia Roberts, and so does she. Cadell says many women are turned on by the idea of playing call girl. Set up a scenario in which she arrives at your door and you negotiate a fee and a program of sexual activities for the night. "Guys agree that it's a big turn-on because they know they'll get their money's worth," says Cadell.

WHAT HER DOG SAYS ABOUT HER
Can you tell if she's the nurturing type? Look at what's licking her ankles. Not you, her dog. Susan Heitler, Ph.D., a clinical psychologist, says that when a woman chooses a dog, "something about that dog needs to resonate with something the woman likes about herself."

The Pocketbook Pup: Maltese, Chihuahua
It means: She loves attention and flouts rules by taking the dog everywhere. John C. Wright, Ph.D., a professor of psychology at Mercer

University, says of such owners, "They're dying to hear, 'Oh, what a darling puppy!'—as though that says something about them."

The Playful Pooch: Labrador, Golden Retriever
It means: She's adventurous, a guy's girl who's not afraid to sweat. A Lab says playful; a golden implies affection—they like to lick, says Heitler. Licking is good.

The Mutt: Could Be Anything
It means: She's bighearted, a rescuer, a woman who looks beneath the surface. "She's very confident and says, 'I see value in you, even though everyone else in the world thinks you're ugly,'" says Wright. Don't take it personally.

The Chic Dog: Pug, Kerry Blue Terrier
It means: She's trendy, possibly superficial, Heitler says. She may have bought it as a fashion accessory without studying its traits, warns Marty Becker, D.V.M., author of *Chicken Soup for the Pet Lover's Soul*.

The Powerhouse: Great Dane, Irish Wolfhound
It means: She likes a challenge—and protection. A powerful dog may mirror her personality. "The hidden agenda may be 'Be careful and don't do anything stupid,'" says Wright.

SWEET SMELL OF THE SEXES
Maybe we've all taken this grooming thing too far. It turns out that a man's perspiration can brighten a woman's mood. In a controlled study, researchers told male volunteers to use fragrance-free soap and skip deodorant for 4 weeks.

Then they applied a blended extract (with the smell disguised) from the men's armpits to the upper lips of 18 women ages 25 to 45.

Results showed they were less tense and more relaxed. "Modulator pheromones" in the sweat influence a woman's mindset, says

George Preti, Ph.D., lead author of the study at the Monell Chemical Senses Center and the University of Pennsylvania. "Women can't buy it," Preti says, "but they may be able to use their boyfriend's undershirt."

Speaking of smell, don't be fooled by the seemingly slender gal wearing the floral-spice fragrance. In a study by the Smell and Taste Treatment and Research Foundation of Chicago, men perceived women to weigh 12 pounds less when the women wore this type of scent. Sexual arousal may make men less objective, says lead researcher Alan R. Hirsch, M.D., who is the neurological director of the Smell and Taste Treatment and Research Foundation in Chicago.

ASK THE GIRL
NEXT DOOR
The honest truth about women
from our lovely neighbor

Different Ex-pectations

My girlfriend's ex keeps calling her. Is there anything I should say or do? —ANONYMOUS

Your girlfriend probably prefers that you let her handle it. I know I would. Everybody deals with exes differently, and unless his calls are negatively affecting your relationship (meaning they're more than just annoying), there's no reason to interfere. When she wants your advice or help, she'll ask for it.

What's Up, G?

Do you know your G-string is peeking out from the top of your hipster pants? Are you doing it on purpose? —DAVE C., FORT LAUDERDALE

Whenever I shop for jeans these days, every pair I try on has a waist so low, my panties become visible the second I move. The only style that doesn't reveal my thong has pleats and a high elastic waistband, which are the denim equivalents of white loafers and a braided belt. What I'm trying to say is that while some women might be flashing their under-garments with flirtatious glee, the rest of us are merely victims of fashion. But really, do you mind?

Toastmaster

Can I impress a woman by making a toast at dinner, or will she think it's lame? —DAN B., BOSTON

I always love it when a guy says, "Cheers," and then looks me in the eye for an intense second before taking the first sip of his first drink of the night. As a matter of fact, if he fails to do that, I'll count it against him. Anything more complicated and you have to be careful or, yes, she'll view your toast as the verbal equivalent of white loafers. I'd hold off on quoting the *Bhagavad Gita* or obscure lines from Jim Jarmusch movies unless you're 100 percent sure your date will get the reference. A safer way to go would be to toast a good thing that happened in her life recently: a new apartment, a finished project at work, her sister's wedding, the amazing parking spot she scored right outside the restaurant—anything that shows you've been paying attention. Another toast that always works: Flash a sincere smile and say, "Here's to you." Just never add "kid" to the end.

Her Faraway Stare

Some women seem to avoid eye contact even though I get a sense that they're interested. Is it shyness? Pride? What?

—ALEX, NORWALK, CONNECTICUT

I've done it myself. I'll spot a good-looking guy in a coffee shop, at the bookstore, or in a bar and immediately pretend he isn't there. My thought: If he's attracted to me and looking to meet someone new, he'll say something. So I'll purposely look in the other direction. Meanwhile, I'm hovering in his vicinity and hoping he'll attempt docking maneuvers. So yes, it's shyness and pride, but mostly it's our annoying, persistent female reluctance to make the first move.

The Ex Factor

Why do women hold on to random stuff that ex-boyfriends gave them? My girlfriend's apartment is like a mausoleum of lovers past.   —HARRY, NEW YORK CITY

Take it as a good sign. The fact that your girlfriend enjoys being reminded of the past probably means that she's had mostly positive, healthy experiences—making your prospects for the future more promising than if there were no evidence of her romantic history at all.

THE DATING GAME

T hink of the worst "single guy" experience you've ever had. Was it a barroom pickup attempt that left your target laughing and your ego wounded? Or maybe a horrid first date filled with awkward pauses, sputtering chemistry, and a clumsy good-night peck that was more kiss of death than actual kiss?

The point is this: You survived it. And thanks to this section, you'll never suffer through anything like that again. Whether it's your first line or your first meal, you're about to learn the surefire techniques used by the most successful guys we know to find, woo, and win the women of their dreams.

Get ready for the best single experience of your life. Read on.

20 Simple Tips for the Perfect Date

Dos and don'ts from a professional matchmaker

BY SAMANTHA DANIELS

1. It's okay to suggest a drink instead of dinner for a first date. She dreads a boring four-course ordeal, too.

2. Call her by early evening on Monday to confirm a Tuesday get-together. (Weekends aren't for first dates.)

3. Leave your home and work numbers. No home number, and she'll assume you have a wife or girlfriend.

4. If you want to keep the plans a surprise, at least clue her in as to what to wear. You do not want an overdressed, over-stressed woman navigating the Talladega pits in high heels.

5. Yes, she'll notice if the date location you've chosen is conveniently around the block from your place.

6. Don't assume that just because you're out with a beautiful woman, she knows how pretty she looks—she wants to hear it from you.

7. Ask if she's too cold or too warm, and if changing the temperature is in your power, fix it.

8. Men judge women according to whether they can picture having sex with them; women judge men by whether they can imagine kissing them. White teeth, fresh breath, and unchapped lips make her more apt to pucker up.

9. Do not ask her, "So, what kind of music do you like?" The last 25 guys asked that. Be original.

10. She loves when you insist on ordering dessert. Sharing = extra-sexy.

11. Tip well: Grab the check, mentally divide the bill by 10, double that number, and throw down the tip. Do it quickly but casually. Believe me, she'll be watching.

12. If she touches your arm, she's interested; if she touches your leg, she's interested tonight.

13. When in doubt, hold her hand.

14. Very small protective gestures go a long way and show her you're a gentleman: Offer your arm as she's stepping from a curb; direct her away from shards of broken glass à la *Say Anything*. She'll notice if you wait until she's safely in her car or house before you leave. Wait the extra 90 seconds, and next time you might be going in with her.

15. She expects you to know her eye color after the first date.

16. Women need momentum—without it, they lose interest or wonder if you have. Momentum = a minimum of one date a week, plus a couple of phone calls in between.

17. She knows that when you invite her over for a homemade meal or to watch a movie, it's code for "Tonight is hookup night." Don't play this card any earlier than date three.

18. A Friday or Saturday night is required by date four. Otherwise, she'll wonder who else you're seeing.

19. Rule of Genital Groping: If anything happens that couldn't be shown on prime-time TV, call her the next day. Otherwise, she'll feel cheap and used.

20. Don't say "I'll call you" if you have no intention to. She'd prefer that you say nothing at all.

Find the Right Line

A bartender's guide to happy-hour hookups

BY CHRIS CONNOLLY

BARTENDERS ARE THE COOLEST. And the coolest bartender at the coolest bar in my neighborhood is Andrew. He settles the arguments, he knows the sports stats, and, most important, he controls the beer taps. He gets paid to do what everyone else is spending money to do: hang out in his bar.

Andrew started at Live Wire, my local house of revelry in San Diego, 2 years ago, and he's been working in bars for a decade. His nose is pushed to one side because of a soccer game head butt, but the ladies say it gives him a sexy edge. Andrew doesn't know everything, but he's willing to offer an opinion on anything. One night he turned to me and said, "Okay, Mike Tyson against a pack of jackals. Who you got?"

"Tyson now?" I asked.

Andrew: "No. In his prime."

Me: "Do the jackals know they're in a fight?"

Andrew: "No. But Tyson's trunks are made of meat."

Me: "Jackals in three."

But the subject Andrew has really mastered is women. He knows what they like, what they don't like, which approach will work on this one, and what will make that one pour a drink on you. I asked him once how he knows so much, and he told me, "The bar is like a one-way mirror. I can stand 8 inches from people while I wash glasses, and they'll just continue their conversation. I hear everything."

One night, Andrew was sizing up some guy's chances with a woman for the amusement of his regulars. "This guy's got no shot."

"Why not?"

"Well, the woman he's hitting on isn't here to meet anyone. She's facing directly into the bar. She's just here to have a drink."

Upon hearing this, I realized that the rest of mankind might stand to benefit from Andrew's expansive knowledge of the bar pickup scene. With a bribe of free magazines, some T-shirts, and a promise to change his name, I persuaded him to let me work alongside him one night to observe. He agreed, and glass was in session.

BARTENDER TIP #1

DON'T BE A DICK

The first thing I learned behind the bar was that people expect you to make them drinks. The second thing I learned: People drink some weird-ass sh---. The very first guy I served requested a gimlet. A gimlet? What is a gimlet? What kind of guy drinks gimlets? I called Andrew for backup, and we quickly devised a plan: I would open beers; Andrew would do everything requiring competence. People would ask me for a dirty fuzzy amaretto on the beach, and I'd grin stupidly and point to Andrew. Which was good because once word circulated that I was strictly special ed, I had a lot of time to pester Andrew with questions.

I started with the obvious: "What's the number one rule for meeting women in bars?"

"There are no rules," he said. "Just don't be a dick."

Fair enough.

BARTENDER TIP #2

GO OUT WITH YOUR GIRLFRIENDS

It wasn't until 2 hours into the night that Andrew dropped his first pearl of wisdom. I was, of course, standing around limply when he walked over. "You want to see someone who's going to hook up tonight, right? See the guy sitting at that table over there with all those women?" He indicated the table with a nod. "I guarantee that he's going home with someone."

"Well, yeah," I said. "He's sitting there with four women."

"No, he's not going home with one of them. They're just his friends or women from work or something. But when a guy goes out with a bunch of women, it signals other women that he's not some kind of knucklehead. When a guy goes out with a group of guys, it means he's on the prowl," he said.

It was true. I later saw Mr. She's-Not-My-Girlfriend-She's-a-Friend-Who's-a-Girl chatting up one of the most spectacular women in the place.

BARTENDER TIP #3

UTILIZE THE "ROMANTIC RETURN"

It didn't take long for me to confirm what I'd suspected: The bartender is in a perfect position to observe the mating rituals of the party public. Looking at a bartender is an indication that you want a drink, so people tend to look around the bartender when he or she's behind the bar. This, in turn, allows the bartender to stare directly at people, almost like a fly on the wall. I'd been observing a nondescript guy for about an hour when he pulled off a great maneuver.

He'd spent the evening alternately watching a ball game on television and eyeing a brunette at a nearby table. She wasn't unaware of

his attention—she had even smiled at him—but she didn't seem completely sold on the idea of talking to Mr. Staring Guy. Eventually, he
paid and left without approaching her. I was about to chalk it up to
cowardice when the door to the barroom opened and he walked back
in and started a conversation with her. About 10 minutes later, he left
again . . . this time with her number.

   I reported what I'd seen to Andrew, and he called this maneuver
the "romantic return." Now, to be fair to Mr. Staring Guy, I can't be
sure the boomerang business was an intentional move, but here's
Andrew's in-game analysis: "Leaving the scene and then returning because you 'just couldn't let this opportunity go by' takes you out of
the Lecherous category and puts you in the Romantic Fool category.
It has a Hugh Grant quality that the ladies go for."

BARTENDER TIP #4

DON'T DANCE (UNLESS IT'S WITH A WOMAN)

As the evening wore on and inhibitions wore away, the TVs were
turned off and the music was turned up. Live Wire isn't a dance bar—
it's shaped like a railroad car, and there's little room to move, even
when it isn't packed. Despite this, there was one guy who insisted on
shaking what his mama had given him. He was tall and handsome,
and even a pretty good dancer. But as he got his groove on, he was also
getting on people's nerves. "That guy has the wrong idea," Andrew
said, looking pityingly at him. "He's trying way too hard. He's a good
dancer, but it's obvious that he's showing off. Now, a smart guy would
turn that to his advantage and open a conversation with a woman by
commenting on that dude."

   I don't know if anyone capitalized on that idea, but I can report
the result of Mr. Happy Feet's extra effort: Predictably, he went
home alone.

BARTENDER TIP #5

HAVE GOOD FOLLOW-UP LINES

The next thing that caught my attention was a guy who started a con-versation with a group of women by approaching one of them and saying, "Don't I know you from somewhere?" In recent times this par-ticular pickup line has become almost a parody of itself—sort of a kitschy, so-bad-it's-good kind of thing. So when this guy got in the door by unironically using the line, I was mystified. I asked Andrew how this could happen.

"One time I heard a guy go up to a woman and say, 'Baby, I wanna be your bra,' and she loved it," he told me. "I've seen crazy things work on women. I think it's because nobody really listens to the first thing you say. Like in everyday greetings, nobody cares whether you say, 'Hi,' 'How are you?' or 'Hello.' It's what you say afterward that makes the conversation. So when you start talking to a woman, unless you say something hideously stupid or offensive right away, you'll probably get in a few more sentences. Guys get too caught up in opening lines, when it's the next few things you say that make or break you."

Turns out, Mr. Déjà Vu got broken. The ladies shot him down and were still kicking his corpse around in conversation an hour later when I cleared away their glasses.

BARTENDER TIP #6

BEWARE OF "OVERFRIENDING"

Even though it annoyed him, I was still firing questions at Andrew, looking for that one home run answer that would sum up the whole pickup scene.

Me: "Should you approach women in groups, or will they just eat you alive?"

Andrew: "It depends on them and on you."

Me: "What can you do with an attractive woman's unattractive friend?"

Andrew: "I don't know. Talk to her?"

No matter how hard I tried to get Andrew to commit to a set of Rules of the Game, he'd derail my attempts by insisting that they didn't exist. So when I asked him, "What's the biggest mistake guys make?"

I expected another evasive answer. Instead, without even looking up from the drink he was making, he said, "Overfriending.

"When guys act like they're just looking for a chat, that's exactly what they wind up with," Andrew said. "Listen, women know what you're up to. They get hit on all the time. So if you pretend you're just a friendly guy, she'll think of you that way. Don't be afraid to get a little sexual when you're talking to women. And don't hide your intentions. It's dishonest, and they can see right through it."

As Andrew was explaining overfriending to me, we made last call, booted out the stragglers, and rounded up the empty glasses. I knew I'd gained a fresh perspective on mating and relating from behind the bar. My night of work was done, but before I retired from bartending, there was one more thing I needed Andrew to explain.

THE GIMLET

   2 oz gin
   1 oz Rose's lime juice

Pour ingredients into a shaker with ice and strain into a cocktail glass. Garnish with a lime wedge.

Actually, it's pretty tasty!

Let Her Pick You Up

Yes, women are cruising for you.
Find 'em, lure 'em, and catch a ride

BY DANIELLA BRODSKY

THERE'S NOTHING SADDER than making that long, lonely walk across the tavern floor, slinking back to your buds after taking your best at-bat—and striking out—with the stacked brunette at the bar. One male friend of mine refers to singles-bar rejection as "winning the Heisman"—after the trophy figurine with the "get out of my face" stiff-arm.

Wouldn't it be easier—and less humiliating—if women were the ones who were out to pick up guys? If men could just lie back in the tall grass and let the banquet come to them, instead of always being on the hunt?

Fact is, women *are* out to pick up men. You've probably been picked up plenty of times without knowing it because we women were smart enough to let you think you were the aggressors all along.

As early as 1976, studies were showing that women often make the first move. Men just aren't aware of these moves because a lot of female flirting techniques (looks, smiles, self-caressing) are less recognizable than the kinds you employ (like actually coming over). More recent studies show that when a woman actually does make the trip, she has a 90 percent success rate.

But remember, we're women, women with all the fears and insecurities and body issues that you men love and hate about us at the same time. So favorable statistics can't stop that 10 percent risk of failure from scaring us out of our stilettos if we're feeling less than confident. "Nobody likes to be turned down, but men have been taught that accepting this risk is part of their role in the mating game," says no less experienced a sex guru than Dr. Ruth Westheimer. "Though times have changed, for a woman to take this risk is much more difficult. If you want a woman to make that first move, you have to lower the risk hurdle as much as possible."

Here's how to stack the deck in your favor so that the stiletto trail across the crowded bar always ends at your stool. And, maybe, at her bed some morning soon.

CLEAR THE RUNWAY FOR APPROACH

No matter how interested she might be, no woman is going to try to drag you out of that in-depth conversation you're having with a dozen friends about the intricacies of the West Coast offense. A whole lot of men talking a whole lot of mumbo-jumbo about the option pass? Too intimidating.

So if you don't want to go home alone, you need to create openings for a potential partner to approach. "Wait until you can gracefully leave the conversation, rotate your body away from the group, and spend some time looking for people who might be looking at you," suggests Michael Cunningham, Ph.D., a psychologist and professor of communication at the University of Louisville. If you're waiting for the group to show up, make the most of your time alone. "Don't sit hunched over your drink; look around and smile and nod at various people, showing you're a friendly person, and therefore not likely to put anyone down," says Dr. Ruth.

USE A PROP

Make it easy by handing her a ready-to-go opener. Props—a popular new book, a slick MP3 player, a high-tech cellular phone—are great conversation starters. Empty-handed? Beeline to the jukebox. She's more likely to approach under the guise of picking songs.

MASTER THE LOOK

When you catch her looking, encourage her with a come-hither gaze. (Practice in the mirror. Do you look like a friendly, intelligent man, or do you look like a guy who should buy a pair of Italian loafers and change his name to Serge? It's a fine line, boys.) "Eye contact works best if it's held for a discreet amount of time, say 3 seconds, broken to look down shyly, and finally reestablished," says Cunningham.

While you're looking to illuminate your Welcome sign, smiles are equally powerful in confirming your interest. "Men have a hard job," says Helen Fisher, Ph.D., an anthropologist at Rutgers University and the author of *The First Sex*. "They have to be approachable and kind, yet they must show the power and status that women are attracted to." To achieve such a complex aura with a smile isn't as rare as you might think: "Throughout the animal kingdom, the 'super smile' (lips fully drawn back to reveal both rows of teeth) signals unquestionable interest in the opposite sex." Posture is another indicator; that chest puffing and back arching you see men resorting to when a hot woman enters the room may seem silly, but it definitely makes their intentions clear. Soften your posture by avoiding indicators of arrogance (like holding your head too far back) or standoffishness (crossing your arms over your chest).

BE TOUCHABLE

Invest in clothing made of quality fabrics. "Women are more likely to touch you if you wear cashmere, linen, or leather," says Valerie Steele, director of the museum at the Fashion Institute of Technology. While men respond visually, women respond to tactile value. "According to a theory in psychology called neurolinguistic programming, people fall into three categories: visual, audio, or kinesthetic (responding to touch)," says Susan Rabin, director of the School of Flirting in New York City and author of *101 Ways to Flirt*. "A lot more women are kinesthetic, and communicate and respond intensely to touch." Also, quality fabrics show good taste and financial security—things women are always attracted to.

> **INSTANT SEXPERT**
>
> ## Don't Let Her Fool You
>
> Breast implantation is surgery; surgery leaves scars. Look for twin scars underneath the breasts, around the nipples, or under the arms, close to the torso. It's more fun than an Easter egg hunt. If she hasn't achieved nudity, check the outline of the top of her breasts. If one or both are perfect semicircles, suspect implants. If all else fails, cop a hug. If they don't compress at all, you're feeling capsules.

ADMIRE HER BALLS

If she appears to be shy and uncomfortable, compliment her boldness by saying, "I'm so glad you came over; I was just working up the courage to introduce myself to you." However, if she seems confident in her appearance (based on her clothing, makeup, hairstyle, and whether or not she's got her hand on your crotch), say something like "I'm amazed you made it to this side of the room with so many guys checking you out."

RECOGNIZE THE SIGNALS

She may have decided that you're the one but may not be willing to risk that long walk across the bar—so she's flashing you the "Walk this way" sign. And it may be going right over your head. "Lots of women complain that men don't get their signals," says Rabin. Research by Monica Moore, Ph.D., a professor at Webster University in St. Louis, indicates that you should look for these clues: glancing around the room, smoothing the hair, and lip licking. The more that women practice flirting, the subtler these clues can be, so pay attention. Look for clusters of these flirting gestures: a few hair tosses and some fidgeting (a sign of sexual tension) in repetition. But be realistic. One hair toss doesn't mean "Come on over, baby"; it means she needs to remove her hair from her eyes.

If she's started the ball rolling with these nonverbal pickup techniques, know how to close the deal: Go over and say, "I find you very attractive. Do you mind if I join you?" But don't ever use a canned line. "She'll feel like you'll use it on anyone, which smacks of dishonesty; plus, it's unimaginative," says Rabin. If you want to compliment her, you're better off with a comment that mentions something specific about her—eye color or a necklace, for example. Your opener should make her feel good.

Otherwise, gesture for her to come on over. Rabin recommends a subtle invitational wave of the fingers over the crowd. If there's a clear path for her to come over, take a few steps in her direction and, with a smiling face, show her it's her turn.

A Headhunter for My Heart

He hung out the Helpmate Wanted sign, but the wrong women applied. It was a case of "I do" or die. So he did what any exec with a recruiting problem would do: He hired a headhunter

BY RON GERACI

SHE'S NOT MY TYPE. But this could be the most important date I've ever had.

I'm sitting across from her, in Dante's Italian restaurant in New York, wondering just what's on her mind. She's a skinny brunette with expensive tastes.

And she may be holding my romantic future in her hand. Or, more precisely, in her Rolodex.

Janis Spindel is a professional matchmaker, a trade she's been plying in the lonely hearts capital of the world since 1993. Haven't you heard? *Sex and the City* is over, in more ways than one.

Spindel's service isn't exactly Match.com. She's pricey. She wants $16,500 to set you up with 12 women in 1 year. Who is fool enough to pay this kind of money? Spindel claims she has 25 to 75 active clients (95 percent of whom are male). She also boasts a contact list of more than 5,000 women, and the majority of them paid her $100 for the chance to get into this database.

Results? "I'm responsible for 508 marriages and 600 committed relationships," Spindel says.

She's just met her next hard-case client.

We're on a fake date. She's noting my looks and posture, my confidence level, and my ability to play the badminton of male-female repartee. She asks pointed questions. What kind of women do you like? Which traits are must-haves? Which are deal breakers?

It's like asking a polar bear what flavor of seal he likes best.

I rattle off qualities that have appealed to me: Pretty. Brunette. Smart enough to use her tongue as a scalpel. Able to laugh and nurse children. It was about as helpful as a Wanted poster that said "white guy."

These are my druthers, but not necessarily my options. Spindel is making her own mental list of female qualities that would suit me, based on what I bring to the table. I'm a journalist, not the CEO of a semiconductor company or a successful plumber. I'm 5'6". And on the "handsome" scale ranging from Dennis Kucinich to George Clooney, I'd have to bribe my way to the halfway mark.

Spindel tells me how she does her voodoo. "It's an instinct—someone will pop into my head, and I may not even know the reason," she says. "In fact, I already have someone in mind for you."

I snap to attention like a Jack Russell hearing a can opener.

"But first we need to get you in shape."

Four days later, Elena Castaneda walked into my life, and apartment. She's a fit, dark-haired beauty with European features and the light, crisp smell of a classy woman in her late thirties. Sadly, this wasn't a date. She's Spindel's image consultant, and she completed her appraisal in 5 seconds, as a woman can.

"Your place is a bachelor cliché," she affirmed. "A lot of metal and glass, a lot of black and gray, everything sterile and cold."

She gave me strict prescriptions: Put carpets on the hardwood floors. Buy softer lighting. Paint the white walls any soft color—the bedroom a different color from the hall or living room. Warm up the place.

We headed into the bedroom. Her look of dismay was familiar.

"Invest in bedding," she said, looking at me as though I could

5 No-Fail Ways to Tell If She's the One

Tick all five boxes below before you size up any woman for carats.

☐ **You'd choose shackles.** "The idea of losing her should be more frightening to you than losing your freedom," says Aline Zoldbrod, Ph.D., a psychologist and sex therapist in Boston. Translated, this means you're able to say, "I am ready to get married," which half the guys who walk down aisles cannot.

☐ **You care about the details of her day-to-day life.** Read it again. It's not going to change.

☐ **She sees you, not your potential.** Make sure she's in love with your "before" photo, and not the "after" pic you may never achieve. "Men want to be appreciated for who they actually are, not who women want them to be," says Carol Kauffman, Ph.D., a psychology instructor at Harvard Medical School. "You shouldn't contort yourself to fit her expectations."

☐ **She fits in with kin.** You shouldn't cringe, even slightly, at the thought of bringing her to a weeklong family reunion or seating her between your boss and an impress-or-die client.

☐ **Your fights work.** You argue a lot and get nowhere? "Take her to bed if you want, but don't commit, and don't bother arguing with her," says Tina B. Tessina, Ph.D., a psychotherapist in Long Beach, California, and the author of How to Be a Couple and Still Be Free. If she's your wife-in-waiting, the occasional (as in not hourly) fight will lead your relationship to a new level, not just another hole in the drywall.

forget anything else she might say that day. A new silk-cotton comforter, lush blankets, 300-thread-count sheets, throw pillows—I needed them like England needs dentistry.

Still unconvinced she was worth $200 an hour (her usual fee

Hello Follies (and successes)

S o much subliminal information is conveyed in those first seconds of contact," says Carol Kauffman, Ph.D., a relationship therapist and a psychology instructor at Harvard Medical School. Okay, so you're on the clock. Make every second count. Below are 10 ways—in rough chronological order—a woman judges your fitness to be her proverbial daddy.

Did he dress well for the date? "She's watching to see if you put some energy into your dress and grooming," says Aline Zoldbrod, Ph.D., a psychologist and sex therapist in Boston. "If you don't take the trouble to dress well for her now, she could see it as disrespectful."

Is he depressed? Does he stare at my breasts? Does he have any sense of humor? If you're a total loser, it pays for her to ascertain that on the first date, says Zoldbrod.

Is he like my ex? Yes, we always pay for the last guy's sins. "What women want is often based on their past negative or positive experiences," says Kauffman.

So when she talks about past boyfriends, heed well.

Is he bitter about past relationships? She needs full use of your closets. There's no room for baggage.

when working with Spindel), I escorted her through my closet. After a grueling 60 minutes that saw the death of many old friends, she gave me 10 specific dressing points all men should employ.

She eyed me for 10 seconds.

"Get rid of your glasses or wear softer frames. Your glasses hide your eyes. Women want to see your eyes. You need to lose 20 pounds. You'll carry yourself completely differently, and you'll wear your clothes much better. Have pride in your hairline. You can tell you're self-conscious about it, and that's much worse than having a receding hairline—go get a hairstyle that doesn't hide it."

Can he talk about himself and listen to me? She'll carry 80 percent of the conversation load. Just make sure your 20 percent is about something.

Is he generous? Women somehow see a correlation between leaving a 10 percent tip and having a propensity to drown kittens.

Does he make me feel understood and appreciated? If you can't succinctly state her values, her politics, and her ambitions, you're probably failing here. Ask more questions. Listen to the answers this time.

Is he open to a relationship but not needy? Ace the other nine criteria here and your odds of appearing needy will edge toward nil.

Does he keep promises? If you're not reliable, you're not viable, especially not for the ultimate goal of all this. . . .

Does he have the potential to be a good father? "For long-term potential, she considers whether you have the values she wants in a man," says Jean Koehler, Ph.D., president of the American Association of Sex Educators, Counselors, and Therapists.

I wondered if I was going to get a buy on penile enlargement.

Meanwhile, Spindel coughed up my first match.

"Her name is Amy," she said on the phone 2 days after Castaneda's strategic strike. She was 33, lived in Connecticut, worked in pharmaceuticals.

I stood watch for her at the mouth of the Oyster Bar in Grand Central Station for 15 minutes after 8:00, eyeing a total of six solo females, my prayers split for and against. Finally, my raised eyebrow found another.

Amy had brownish blonde hair and stood about 5'2", with a

body between good and rockin'. She had the face of an innocent, let's-eat-s'mores-on-Friday-night girl. Her eyes were so large and so blue you couldn't avert your gaze. They were ocean blue. And big.

"Your eyes are incredibly blue," I ventured later as she tenderly forked her whitefish.

"I get that a lot," she said, embarrassed, looking at her lap.

The advantages of having a matchmaker were immediately apparent. Spindel was our ice-breaking conversational ploy, and she also gave us more psychic glue than relying on our own faulty judgments. A high-end shaman of hookups thought we had romance potential!

"So? So?" Spindel pressed, ringing me when I got home, shortly before midnight.

"Amy's terrific," I replied. "But my male intuition tells me that she wants a low-key, stay-at-home guy who will get married soon and give her a safe, reliable life." I paused to think where exactly the negatives were in this.

"What did Amy say about the date?" I asked; that's another advantage of having a high-priced matchmaker.

"She didn't really say anything negative. . . . She had a good time," Spindel answered.

I could tell this was between a half-truth and a lie, but she wouldn't elaborate. She recommended a second date with Amy.

"Can we continue to scout as well?" I asked. "I'm not getting any younger."

For match number two, Spindel served up Ariel, an athletically built 27-year-old with brown hair and a pretty, tomboyish face. We met at a fancy Chinese restaurant for a long lunch. I couldn't determine whether Ariel's casualness was the mark of a laid-back girl or a lack of interest in me. Naturally I assumed the first. Ariel said she was a novelist and was constantly traveling, and vague details led me to suspect a trust fund was in the picture. An hour later, on the corner of Forty-eighth and Third, she hugged me quickly into her ski jacket like she was saying goodbye to a nephew who was getting on a plane.

I called Spindel for the postgame wrap-up. "It wasn't happening for her," she allowed. "That's the way it is sometimes."

A few days later, I had the rematch with Amy at a trendy Italian restaurant. For 2 hours, it was like pulling conversation out of an oil painting. It sucked hard.

I told Spindel as much.

She shot back, "Okay, she didn't like the first date; you didn't like the second. That means we need a third date."

"Why didn't you tell me before how she felt about the first date?" I asked.

"For what purpose?" Spindel replied. "She wasn't sure. Now she's definitely interested."

I saw her point but had the feeling that my hired counsel was in cahoots with the prosecution, too. I wanted disclosure.

Match number three was Chloe, a 35-year-old publishing executive who had 60 people reporting to her but zero reporting to her bedchamber. She was beginning to panic about her unborn children.

We met for a bite after work. She told me she wanted a serious relationship and marriage, but had momentum in her job and didn't know if she'd have time for either. Dollars and new responsibilities were flying in. We both sipped our drinks; the colossal drawback to her argument—her lack of outside interests—made its point during the silence.

Men are intimidated by high-achieving women, Chloe added. They run, searching for partners they can handle. I've heard untold numbers of women say this, but it's only half the story. Men judge women on their mothering quotient. At least I have. If you're marrying June Lockhart, you know the kids will be all right. Join forces with Condi Rice and it gets a little fuzzy.

"Will I hear from you again?" Chloe said suspiciously, hugging me after I opened the cab door for her.

"Yes," I said, weirded by her suspicion. She heard from me the next day.

The day after that, she was off to her Madrid office for a month, then to the West Coast for some time after that. My matchmaker couldn't pin her down for the date postmortem.

"You're having crappy luck, aren't you?" Spindel said. "A lot of my clients have success after three matches. Most are in a committed relationship within 90 days."

"Crappy luck?" I repeated. With just these three particular girls? She was insinuating I was the stick in the spokes here. Which I was, I suppose, somehow. I realized a major disadvantage to my journalistic test-drive of Spindel's service: I wasn't paying full boat, so I had none of the frustrated urgency of a man who's just shelled out $16,500 and has a dwindling number of at-bats with each miss. Paying a ridiculous price for something makes you value it more. Look at Iraq.

"I can bring the horse to water, but I can't make him drink," Spindel said, referring to my fickleness with Amy and inability to wow the panties off Ariel. "You know, matchmaking takes a great deal of effort and time."

I felt like apologizing for not having proposed to Amy yet, or having hopped a jet to Spain and kidnapped Chloe out of a board meeting. It was an interesting trap, because by the time men are old enough to afford a five-figure fee, they've had enough female failures to accept blame without question.

Smarting from two train-wreck pairings, and maybe a bit frustrated—having invested effort by now, if not equity—I needed an ego salve.

I dialed Amy.

"I'm so glad to hear from you," she said, waking up from a nap. "I was thinking of you, and I don't think coincidences are random."

We had a third date. And two more. She made me feel good. There could be the mustard seed of a relationship. We're not ideal, but we're not absurd. Maybe that's how it starts, instead of the Big Ben tolling of fate I've always been searching for.

On the other hand, a broken clock is right twice a day.

But Spindel's first hunch wasn't hooey. For $16,500, it would have been genius.

Your Blind Date

Step one: Remove blindfold. (Or not. Your call.)
Here's how to reduce the stress of an awkward setup

BY BILL STIEG

BLIND DATES ARE LIKE any first date, only scarier. That's why we avoid them. A first date has enough baggage without adding a trunkful of unknowns: What does she look like? Is she easygoing or tightly wound? High or low maintenance? Jeans or a skirt—and if it's jeans, are they Levi's or Armani Exchange? Does she laugh easily, and does her laugh sound like Kate Hudson's or Fran Drescher's? And again—not that we're shallow—what does she look like? On a normal date, you've sussed this out already, well before making the call. But let's say you've finally caved in to Aunt Bernie's request to take out her neighbor's daughter. Fear not. Heed the words of Helen Keller: "Life is either a daring adventure, or nothing." You've tried nothing. Time for adventure. This could be the start of something wonderful. So let the word go out to friends and relations: You're ready to be set up. But first, read the advice below.

Remember, on a blind date, she's as clueless as you are. Increase the likelihood of success—or at least a tolerable time—by following a few rules from Gabe Fischbarg, author of *The Guide to Picking Up Girls*, and Roger Lodge, host of the syndicated show *Blind Date*.

DECODE. You're no saint; you want to know what she looks like. Ask your matchmaker specific questions. "Women are never accurate when describing their friends—they always think a girl is prettier than she is," Fischbarg says. "'Nice' might mean unattractive, and

The Other Kind of Blind Date . . .

In a trusting relationship, a blindfold in bed can kink-start a stalled sex life. "It may enhance a person's feelings of vulnerability and surrender, which may be arousing," says Katherine Rachlin, Ph.D., a sex therapist and psychologist. Licensed clinical sexologist Gloria Brame, Ph.D., calls it an "incredibly sensual" sexual exercise for men and women. "It forces you to focus on your body's pleasure because you're not being distracted by visual stimuli." Try the soft-foam Mindfold, $20 (mindfold.com).

'curvy' might mean full-figured." Best bet: Ask a guy friend to set you up.

CALL. "You can e-mail back and forth, but at some point you need to call her," says Fischbarg. It's more personal, and the date will go more smoothly if you've gotten the boring what-do-you-do stuff out of the way.

LUNCH. "The key to any blind date is that you want to do it during the day," says Lodge. You can bail without looking like a jerk: You have a meeting to get to. After-work drinks are the next-best option, says Fischbarg. At the beginning of the date, tell her you have somewhere else to be later in the evening.

HOW TO BAIL. If you have less chemistry than Jacko and Lisa Marie, take a trip to the bathroom and covertly ask for the check to be brought to the table promptly. "You can eat or drink at a normal pace, but you've cut out 15 minutes," Fischbarg says. The prearranged call from your buddy is too obvious.

NO SEX. Lodge sees lots of men bomb on *Blind Date*. "I cannot emphasize this enough: Never, ever be the first one to bring up sex," Lodge says. "If she wants to go there, let her bring it up. And even if the date is going really well, don't get physical. Walk her to her car or door and give her a hug. You'll leave some mystery."

Stretch: Portrait of a Serial Seducer

Love lessons from a dog groomer who lives in a trolley car?
Form an orderly queue, gentlemen

BY CHRIS CONNOLLY

M**EN, MEET YOUR MASTER.** He's a scruffy, cantankerous transport from "the ATL" (that's Hot-lanta, to you Yanks) called Stretch, and he lives in a trolley car behind my house in San Diego. The trolley car was sunk into a hillside about a decade ago and converted into a living room/kitchen. It's connected by three stairs to a small outpost containing a bedroom and a bathroom, and when I sit out in my garden to write, Stretch frequently sticks his head out the bathroom window to talk. Since I spend a lot of time writing and Stretch spends a lot of time in the bathroom, I've learned many things about him. He's 25, works at My Beautiful Dog-O-Mat as a groomer, and dog-sits neighborhood pups for extra cash. He has long brown hair, wears the same pair of jeans with the pocket falling off every day, and eats mostly 99-cent Chinese chicken that tastes like it's been breaded in Lucky Charms. Oh, and one more thing: He can get any woman he wants.

I've never seen a man attract more women than Stretch does. But I have on more than one occasion seen a beautiful woman stop by the trolley for a "visit," only to find another, equally beautiful woman already inside. I've never seen Stretch agonize about how to approach a woman. But I have seen him pick up two women at a concert by burping at them. Stretch may seem an unlikely seduction guru, but hey, Yoda ain't too impressive at first blush either.

So, what does Stretch know that other guys don't? I decided to observe him for a few weeks to see what I could learn. As I watched, I brought up dating and romance in conversation as much as I could, and even ran my observations by Lisa Daily, a dating coach and the author of *Stop Getting Dumped.* The following, in Stretch's own words, are the results of my study.

STRETCH SECRET #1

"STRETCH DON'T CHASE CHICKS. CHICKS CHASE STRETCH."

When Stretch first said this to me, I laughed. Then I realized that it's true. He doesn't chase women. He'll approach them, sure, but he doesn't go out of his way to impress any woman. He makes his intentions clear, then leaves the decision making to her. If she likes him, that's great. But more important, if she doesn't like him, that's great, too. Obviously, he'd prefer that she respond positively, but like all successful seducers, once he lays his cards out on the table, he's prepared to deal with the results.

"It comes down to confidence," says Daily, who is also the founder of stopgettingdumped.com. "There's something very sexy about someone who can take you or leave you."

Of course, we're not all blessed with such self-confidence, but that's not an insurmountable problem, according to Daily. "It is possible to 'fake it till you make it,'" she says. "The perception of confidence has a lot to do with the approach. Less confident men will spend half the night seeking eye contact. With a confident guy, it's three looks and he's in."

So if you want to enter Stretchdom, project confidence and act quickly. If you find yourself thinking, "Did she just . . . ?" you're already too late.

STRETCH SECRET #2

"STRETCH ONLY LIKES WOMEN STRETCH LIKES."

While Stretch won't turn down offers from women who approach him, he won't extend himself unless he's really interested. Although it's doubtful he's read it, a study published in the *Personality and Social Psychology Bulletin* suggests that Stretch is onto something.

The study found that people look for relationship partners who provide them with self-verification or self-enhancement. This means we're attracted to relationship partners who see us as we see ourselves (verification) or to people who find us more attractive than we find ourselves (enhancement). Pursuing only people you're boom-box-over-the-head crazy about plays into this perfectly. If you go after only women whom you find really, really attractive, they'll sense how much you desire them and respond positively. When you aim low and settle for someone you're not crazy about, you'll lower your chances of success and also risk being rejected by someone you didn't really like in the first place. Ouch.

STRETCH SECRET #3

"STRETCH LIKES THE DA-DONKA-DONK!"

If my descriptions of Stretch as a bummy, slummy, chicken-eating weirdo have given you the wrong impression, let me set things straight: He's one sexy bastard. And by sexy, I mean sexual. He exudes sexuality, according not only to the women in line outside the trolley but also to Daily. Successful seducers make sure women see them as potential sex partners. A 2002 phone survey revealed that fully 50 percent of people do not see their opposite-sex friends as potential sex partners. So one thing Stretch and other lady-killers avoid is being categorized this way. "If you try to sneak in with a woman by being friends," says Daily, "you'll project that, and you'll end up as friends."

STRETCH SECRET #4

"STRETCH DON'T LIE. HONESTLY."

Actually, that is a lie. Stretch lies all the time. "My family owns a castle." "I must have been going 120." "I had 30 beers." And on and on. But those are guy lies. When it comes to women, Stretch is a regular George Washington.

Daily condones this approach. "If you lie to a woman about anything—your intentions, where you see the relationship going, anything—it can trip you up," she confirms. It goes back to confidence. When you know you've been up-front with a woman, you can actually avoid most entanglements that would ensue if you'd been lying to her along the way. Stretch is unerringly honest with the women he dates. He tells them what he wants and what he doesn't want, what he likes and what he doesn't like. He agrees with them honestly, and more important, he disagrees with them honestly. Come to think of it, it's downright sneaky how honest he is.

STRETCH SECRET #5

"STRETCH INTERESTS PEOPLE BY BEING INTERESTING."

I guess in the right situation, with the right lighting and music, Stretch might strike the right person as handsome. Yet it's clearly not his looks that draw women to him. Unless you're Brad Pitt, your personality is far more important than your baby blues. You hear all the time that a sense of humor is the key to success with women, and it's certainly great if you can make witty, disarming comments that leave the assemblage in stitches. But for most guys, "sense of humor" translates more closely to making people smile than to making people crack up. It's about gumption, not guffaws. Stretch isn't funny in a stand-up kind of way. If he tried to be, he'd come off as a big fake. What he is, though, is an undeniable personality. Recently, he wore a bunny suit—yes, a bunny suit—to a Flaming Lips concert. He made a huge splash, got in the newspaper, and met a ton of women.

Now, I'm not suggesting you attempt the Great Plushie Ploy. But eventually, you're going to need something to talk about, and you could do worse than "Remember that time you wore your bunny suit to a Flaming Lips concert?" for a conversation starter.

STRETCH SECRET #6

"STRETCH DON'T MAKE RULES."

People who establish rules regarding whom they'll date are making a big mistake, say both Stretch and Daily. "I don't date actresses." "I don't date people from the office." If Cameron Diaz started temping in your office and wanted to date you, you'd break those rules in a second, so why make them at all? The only rule successful seducers obey is "Thou shalt not date family." They're open to everyone else.

STRETCH SECRET #7

"IF YOU WANT TO TOUCH A WOMAN, YOU HAVE TO TOUCH HER."

When it comes to women, Stretch is touchy-feely. Not in a creepy way, but in a way that takes all the inhibitions out of physical contact.

"Successful seducers initiate contact fairly early, in a nonthreatening way," Daily says. It can be something as simple as taking a woman's hand to help her out of a car or placing your hand lightly on her back as she goes through a doorway. Just make sure to create physical contact in the first few minutes of any encounter so it doesn't develop into "a thing." "Try touching a knee or an arm," Daily advises. Stretch plays with hair and initiates thumb-wrestling matches. It's never calculated, and therefore it's never creepy. And it makes everything later on much less tense.

STRETCH SECRET #8

"STRETCH DON'T HAVE ROUTINES."

Stretch has met women at bus stops, at dog parks, at police stations, on Chinese junks, everywhere. In fact, he credits a lot of his success to his openness to meeting women anywhere. "If you go to the same club every Friday, you're only going to meet the people who go to that club every Friday," he says. Daily concurs: "Shoe stores are great on Friday nights because it's easy to start conversations."

You: "Are these too funky for the head of a Fortune 500 company?"

Gorgeous brunette (melting): "N-no . . . "

Or take a girl pal to your next office party and introduce her to the single guys you work with. Then have her return the favor. It's a great way to meet like-minded people, says Daily.

STRETCH SECRET #9

"DON'T IGNORE THE TEACHER JUST BECAUSE HE'S WEARING A BUNNY SUIT."

You know what they say about rabbits and reproduction.

The 112-Lb. Pickup

It's easy to find panting, half-naked women at the gym. The hard part
is getting anywhere with them. Here's the road map

BY JENNIFER BENJAMIN

IT'S YOUR MOVE

You love that feeling: both of you drenched in sweat, short of breath,
flushed, and spent from exertion. But now you have to think of
something to say. It should be natural: The gym seems an ideal spot
to find someone to share a smoothie with, considering all the exposed flesh and sexual posturing (she's on the thigh adductor again!),
plus a common interest in fitness. And it's not just a guy thing;
there's a good chance she has mentally slipped off your CoolMax
shorts.

"A woman's estrogen level rises and sexual fantasies increase
during a strenuous workout," says Robert S. Brown, M.D., Ph.D., a
professor of psychiatric medicine at the University of Virginia School
of Medicine. "That, in conjunction with enhanced cheerfulness and
arousal, along with lowered hostility, anger, and stress during exercise,
makes some women more approachable." Key word: "some."

As a personal trainer at Bally Total Fitness in New York City,
Nikki Kimbrough has seen plenty of guys shot down. A guaranteed
loser move: interrupting a woman's workout. "That can be insulting
because she's there to work out, not necessarily to get hit on." Try
these tips to further elevate her heart rate.

WHEN

Wait until I get off the treadmill. Like I'm going to puff and
yell to talk, then trip and fall on my face? —ANGELA, 25, ARTIST

To work out, I usually wear an old college tee or one I think is
funny, so I like when a guy asks about my shirt. It's a conversation starter. —MARIA, 36, EDITOR

HOW

I feel totally flattered if he asks me to spot him. It means he doesn't see me as some dainty weakling. —ALICE, 28, TEACHER

Instead of being all superior and telling me what I'm doing wrong on a machine, nicely ask if I want a better way to work that muscle, so I don't feel like a big loser. —JENNY, 26, COPYWRITER

WARNINGS

If she's wearing headphones, staring intently at CNN or a magazine, not even a shirtless Tiki Barber could get her attention.
—NIKKI KIMBROUGH

Sorry, I don't want to talk to you if you're dripping sweat. Wipe yourself off before trying to pick me up. —ANA, 27, WAITRESS

If I've just heard you grunting in the weight room like a walrus, there's no way I'll talk to you.
—NINA, 24, FLORIST

I may be confident in my body, but I don't want to hear any comments about it or feel like you're staring down my shirt or at my butt—even if you just saw me do "downward dog" in yoga. —ALISHA, 30, LAWYER

INSTANT SEXPERT

The Best Ways to Tell If a Woman Is Interested in You

You spot her across a crowded room. She smiles. You smile. Now what?

1. Approach her from the side. This makes you less threatening and increases her interest.
2. Keep your eyes above her neck.
3. Wait for a break in conversation. Forget clever lines. Say hi. Give her your name. Ask for hers. Talk to her like a relative you actually get along with. She's reluctant? Don't give up. Both men and women are overly ready to think they're being rejected.
4. Leave—briefly. Don't promise to be back; just say, "Excuse me a minute—I have to catch up with my friend. It was great meeting you."
5. Return to your pals for roughly 10 minutes or so. Stay out of her line of sight.
6. Approach her again. If she seems happy to see you, you're in.

Something Old, Something New

A conversation with three guys who date older women

JUST A FEW DECADES AGO, men who dated or married older women were considered oddities. Today, they're fast becoming part of the mainstream. According to the U.S. Census Bureau, 12 percent of all marriages are between older women and younger men. And an AARP survey has shown a third of single women ages 40 to 69 date younger men regularly.

In an effort to get our hands around this "age-old" issue, we asked three regular guys—Mike Morris, 25; Ravi Gogte, 26; and Larry Willey, 29—to pull back the sheets on their relationships. Here's what they told us.

You guys are the envy of many American men. How did you get to be so lucky?

Morris: Michelle and I met online. I wrote her, and she wrote back. She's attractive, for one thing. She had a picture of herself in the snow, in snowshoes, going through the woods.

Willey: We were at John Harvard's. She was in the restaurant with her sister and sister-in-law. She was one table away. We had the same waiter, and she sent over a beer.

Gogte: We met at a neighborhood bar, hanging out on a Friday night after work. We didn't notice each other early on. We were sitting at adjacent tables. I was there with my roommate; she was there with her sister. A bachelorette party rolled into the bar and moved the four of us all onto another table. That's how we started talking. We were pretty entertained by the bachelorette party. That broke the ice. Neither of us thought we'd start dating.

How did you end up together?
Gogte: Alcohol had a little bit to do with it that first night. I made a bet with her about something. Then I bet I lived closer to the bar, and she bet she lived closer. And so we had to go back to somebody's place to find out.

When did you find out how old she was?
Morris: I knew before we met because it gives the age online.

Gogte: I had to pull out my ID for something, and she found out my age. Then I found out hers. When I found out she was 40, I didn't believe it. She did not look it. I thought maybe early thirties. When I found that out, I was intrigued and interested and excited. It's nothing I've ever experienced before. I thought it'd be interesting to see where it went.

Because she could afford the bar tab?
Gogte: She did end up buying the drinks.

What was the beginning of your relationship like?
Morris: Intense sexually. Intense attraction.

Gogte: Definitely a good learning experience, both sexually and emotionally.

Did you fear she was using you for your body?

Morris: At first, I think that was her intent, for me to be a boy toy, but things progressed into something more.

And you were up-front about that?
Morris: We were both up-front about that. That's what's great about older women. Talking with someone my age, it would be awkward. She'd be worried about social implications. With Michelle, she said, "This is what I want." And I thought, Sure. But now we're still hanging out.

Gogte: A lot less game playing. We pretty much both went into this relationship with the same expectations. Neither of us was looking for anything very serious. We were both having fun.

Did your friends have fun with it, too?
Willey: You know, the usual chidings. They gave me a hard time when we met because somebody approached me at a bar. One guy said, "All you do is eat and you pick up women." But a lot of my friends at the time were at least 5 years older. The age difference didn't seem like a big deal.

Morris: I told my friends right away about Michelle and her age. Before Michelle, I dated a woman who was 40. She was my one of my photography clients. My friends know I like older women, so that broke the ice. They've all met Michelle, and they think she's cool. All they care about is that I'm happy.

Gogte: The older guys were definitely jealous, the younger guys not so much. The guys who were in the late thirties, early forties— they liked the ability to have a casual relationship with an older woman who knew what she was doing. Experience did make a difference when we were together. That was a lot of fun, and the older guys appreciate that. Most of the friends my age looked at me a little weird. The age was just too much for them. They were thinking a lot of their moms were only a couple years older. It made a difference to them.

But not to you?

Gogte: I thought it would be interesting if my mom met her because I thought they'd have a lot to talk about. She never met any of my family. I told my mom one time, just to see her reaction, and she was okay with it. She said, "Well, as long as you're having fun and you know what you're getting into."

Morris: She's met my parents. One of my buddies was doing a fund-raiser for a charity. I took off in the event and didn't do any of the work. She tracked down my dad and said hello. If I was nervous to begin with, there's a good chance I shouldn't be introducing her to my parents. Ultimately, older women know what they want, they're up-front about it, and they don't play games.

What traits in you do you think appealed to each of your girlfriends?

Morris: Michelle, in particular, is goofier than me, and I act like I'm 12. And Michelle appreciates that. We have that connection that way. In terms of acting different, there's no difference in age. The only differences in age are when I use slang words that are more my generation and she'll be, like, "What does that mean?"

Gogte: We just joked around about it. People don't always know I'm kidding. She knew I was joking and dished it right back.

I thought older women went for guys who were more mature.

Morris: I have a lot of things going in my life right now: I'm driven. I have my own business. If you were to measure maturity in that way, then I'm mature. It's just that I like to goof off and not get old. Just because you're older doesn't mean you're attracted to someone who's mature. Either you want someone mature or you want someone who's a goof. That doesn't change with age.

Have you ever been self-conscious about the age difference?

Willey: Christine's always mistaken for younger than she is. I'm always mistaken for being older than I am. I don't think anyone can tell.

Morris: The places we've been to, it's been with my friends, and they're cool with it. Every time we go out together, she gets carded because she's with me. I have a baby face, and I always get carded. So they card her, and she gets excited.

Gogte: That was never a big deal, going out. You could tell I was younger, but it didn't seem like I was 17 years younger. Maybe 10 years. I was more concerned with people who actually knew the age difference. In general, I never hung out with her and my friends. It was kind of weird. My friends gave me a lot of grief. It was never malicious. Sometimes when I would hang out with her and her friends, I knew they were thinking, Wow, he's half her age. Though none of her friends ever said anything to me about it.

Whose place would you go to?
Morris: She lives by herself, and it's better to be at her place because of the privacy.

Gogte: I usually went to her house. We were within walking distance of each other, so it wasn't a big deal either way. Her place was nicer than mine. I didn't think it was right to make her walk at night to my place. It was also easier to deal with because my roommates would try to mess with me. She was more comfortable at her place, anyway.

Friends say older women are attractive because they're more comfortable with themselves.
Gogte: That goes back to the whole playing games. You don't really reveal everything that you're holding when you're younger. She definitely didn't hold on to stuff. She'd put it out in the open. She was more comfortable with herself. I was more comfortable with her because of that.

Morris: I've always been attracted to older women. In high school, I always wanted friends' older sisters. Back in my landscaping days, we loved to go mow the lawns of the yummy moms. Now a lot of them are at a point where they have more direction, they're comfortable with themselves, and they understand that I'm a pretty busy person. I work as a mechanical engineer, I train for adventure races, I have a photography business. Older women understand that more, and they don't get huffy about it. Those over 30 are more independent. They've established themselves. They have a life. They know how much time there is in the day.

So, in the end, does the age difference affect the relationship?
Willey: Like any other difference, it's only a big deal if you make it a big deal. We've been married 8 months.

Gogte: The age was a major reason I wouldn't stay in the long run.

Wasn't age was part of what attracted you in the first place?
Gogte: In the long run, I'm thinking of marriage, though I'm not ready right now. If we were to have kids 5 years from now, she'd be 45, which is a bit old to start having kids. My ideal relationship would be with someone that I can grow old with. If she beats me to it, it wouldn't be the same. I wouldn't rule out dating someone older, though.

Any advice for gents trying to pick up the older woman?
Gogte: Go in with an open mind. If you're comfortable as a person and you get along, a lot of the imperfections just melt away. With anybody, it's hard to find everything you're looking for. Have fun, and be open and be honest. There's always some sort of mystery and appeal that a lot of people have. They may not say it or act on it, but at leas for me, there was the intrigue and allure of an older woman. The something sophisticated. The maturity level is much different.

Morris: I think girls between the ages of 18 and 22 are such a pain. All they want to do is get drunk every night. The girls between 23 and 26 are in midlife crisis mode. If you want a girl who knows what she wants and won't play games, be yourself. If you try to act older, they'll see right through that. If you're a goofball, like I am, you'll find a goofball regardless of age. Except with an older woman, you'll know it right away because she'll tell you.

QUICKIES

New Mating Rituals

If online dating or your dance moves aren't working, it might be time to try one of these new ways to date.

Dinner in the Dark (www.dinnerinthedark.com)

THE SETUP: A group of strangers drink and dine in a pitch-black, swanky restaurant. Waiters in night-vision goggles complete the romantic mood.

EXPERT TAKE: "You can explore a mental connection," says Lisa Daily, a dating coach and the author of *Stop Getting Dumped.* But the physical connection may fade in daylight.

The Quiet Party (quietparty.com)

THE SETUP: Women and men gather at a club and communicate solely through written notes. Talking is verboten, unless you excuse yourself to the "whisper room."

EXPERT TAKE: "Silent dating brings teenage flirting back," says Logan Levkoff, a sexologist in New York City. "Passing notes like a teenager may be fun, but it can also be frustrating."

Eight at Eight (8at8.com)

THE SETUP: Dinner parties with four women, you, and three other guys.

EXPERT TAKE: "It allows you to meet a few eligible people without the pressures of an intimate conversation or strained dialogue," says Levkoff.

Proximity Dating

THE SETUP: A dating service that uses advanced mobile phone technology to pinpoint your location. Your phone alerts you when a compatible person comes within a few blocks.

EXPERT TAKE: "It's all the rage in Japan," says Daily. What's not to love about instant gratification?

READING DISC

Here's a first-date move: Let her play with your radio dial. Or have her choose the CD—you'll learn something. Musical tastes are strong personality indicators, a University of Texas study confirms. Study coauthor Peter J. Rentfrow explains what her music choices mean.

SHE PICKS POP, COUNTRY, OR CHRISTIAN. She's outgoing, and if you get a flat tire, she'll probably get out the jack. (She enjoys helping others.) But don't expect anything kinky—she's a traditionalist.

SHE WAILS ON AIR GUITAR. Rock chicks are curious risk takers who like physical challenges. Just don't assume she's a head-banging bimbo: Fans of intense, rebellious music give themselves high marks for intelligence.

SHE FLIPS TO HIP-HOP, SOUL, OR FUNK. Not contemplative, but maybe you figured that out. People into rhythmic, energetic tunes are chatty rule breakers with a strong forgiving side.

SHE'S A FOLK, JAZZ, OR CLASSICAL FAN. While she may be open to new experiences, she'll likely be reluctant to get sweaty (think art film, not Frisbee golf). And if you talk politics, she'll lean to the left.

FIRST WATCH

Women watch closely on the first date. Follow these rules and you're sure to get a second.

Maybe you were charming when you met her (you scored digits, ...d maybe you're witty on the phone. But the real challenge "In the initial dating stages, everyone is on their best ...ssina, Ph.D., a psychotherapist and the author ...ating Again. "So if you do something that ...en a little bit, she's going to wonder how ...n the road." Sometimes your best-intentioned behavior sabotages you. Below, you'll find some surprising—and surprisingly common—mistakes.

YOU THINK YOU SHOULD: Let her decide what to do.

YOU SHOULD: Take charge. Offer at least two suggestions for plans so you're still asking for her input. "Like it or not, taking the lead sends an evolutionary signal that you can take care of her, and women evaluate men on their ability to lead and take care of them," explains Perry Buffington, Ph.D., author of *Cheap Psychological Tricks for Lovers*.

YOU THINK YOU SHOULD: Be friendly to the waiter.

YOU SHOULD: Not go overboard. Of course, you don't chew out a waiter because your steak is overdone, but don't be too charming, especially if your server is wearing a skirt. "When a guy is schmoozing, he comes across as insecure," warns Tessina. "It gives the impression that he needs everyone to like him, not just the woman he's with." Be pleasant, but save the smooth talk for the one you're with.

YOU THINK YOU SHOULD: Ask her about herself.

YOU SHOULD: Actually listen. Tessina says make sure you know these five facts before you say good night: her best friend's name, her work responsibilities, her career plans, what she does for fun, and when she last saw her family. "Whenever we talk about ourselves, we assume the listener likes us, so getting her chatting will reap you rewards as a good date," Buffington says. Score major points by calling her later and mentioning one of the facts you remembered. You were listening, right?

YOU THINK YOU SHOULD: Show you understand her.

YOU SHOULD: Not play Dr. Phil. Yes, a woman loves to feel that you have a direct link to her subconscious, but when you tell her, "You're the kind of girl who . . . ," all you're going to do is piss her off. "It belittles her, oversimplifies her, and makes her self-conscious," says Tessina, "regardless of whether you're being flattering or not." Just pay attention to what she's telling you; she'll feel you're tuned in.

ASK THE GIRL NEXT DOOR
The honest truth about women from our lovely neighbor

Tell and Ask
What's the best way for a guy to ask whether a woman has a boyfriend? —ROB, AUSTIN, TEXAS

Say this: "I want to ask you out, but I suspect you're already seeing someone. Am I right?"

Operation: Digit Retrieval
Okay, so I'm in a bar and trading glances with a great-looking woman, and I want to get her number. What's the best approach?
—KRIS, VIA E-MAIL

I'm most impressed by guys who can casually start a conversation without using a pickup line or offering to buy me a drink. Just a few nights ago, a cute stranger asked me to look closely at the TV screen and tell him who had the bigger butt, Derek Jeter or Roger Clemens. (I said Clemens, of course.) And we ended up talking for hours.

If a woman is making eye contact with you, she obviously does think you're cute enough. If you're too timid to walk up and talk to her, try this move: After catching her eye at least three times, walk over to the bar or the jukebox alone and wait until she looks at you. When she does, flash her a shy smile, tilt your head questioningly, and make a beckoning motion with your hand to let her know you want her to join you.

If she doesn't, no big deal—it's a silent, painless rejection. But the odds are she'll come scampering.

Buy, Used

The woman I'm dating is available only once a week. When we do go out, it's to an expensive dinner, and she offers up nothing but a good-night peck. Is she using me? —HOWIE, SEATTLE

All signs point to yes. When you think about it, you're providing the services of a male escort, only she's getting the free meal. When a woman is hot for a guy, she'll rearrange even a busy schedule to see him a couple of times a week. And by week two, her tongue is sure to participate in the goodbye kiss.

It looks to me as if you're her backup—the lackey she keeps around for when the dating well is dry. Find that insulting? Ditch her. Or, if you like her company and don't mind ponying up for dinner, use her until you find a better option.

Late-Night Ladies

You said that women do actually go out to get laid. How do I know which ones they are? —PATRICK, VIA E-MAIL

You don't. Not until the end of the night, that is. Most women flirt like demons whether or not they're looking to take a guy home, so that's no indication. What can give a horny gal away is how late she sticks around at a bar or party. There's that point when the place starts clearing out and most women who aren't looking for action will head home. But the randier among us will be reluctant to leave if there's someone there we'd like to hook up with. So if the clock strikes 2 A.M., the crowd is thinning, and the girl you've been swapping innuendo with all night is getting more smiley and touchy-feely by the minute, you're golden.

Kiss and Find Out

How can I tell if a woman is interested in me right when I meet her?

—JONATHAN, RYE, NEW YORK

Here are the guidelines: Check out her smile. Does it look as if she couldn't stop grinning if she tried? Check out her eyes. Are they focusing on you and then shyly darting down or off to the side before zeroing in on you again? Check out her hands. Is she fidgeting? Check out her body. Is she standing close to you or leaning toward you and not moving away? Check off all of the above, and you can be sure she's interested.

Running Pass

When I run in the park, I pass an amazing number of knockout-gorgeous women. But how in the world do you stop a woman who's running and try to get somewhere?   —DAVIS, BOULDER, COLORADO

Clothesline her, stupid. Just kidding. You can't stop her. All you can do is keep her in your sights and be there when she slows down. Then pop the most innocent question of all time: "Excuse me—do you know what time it is?" When she answers (even if it's "Sorry, I'm not wearing a watch"), say, "God, why does time go by so slowly when you're running?" What you're really doing is letting her get a good look at your friendly eyes and sweaty physique. If she likes what she sees, she'll make conversation. If she doesn't, she'll give you a short answer, smile, and move on. Short of clotheslining someone, that's about as painless as it gets.

Chemistry or History?

If there's no chemistry on a first date, should I bother going on a second one?   —GARRETT, VIA E-MAIL

How open is your calendar? If you have free Saturday nights to spare, go ahead and give her another try. But let's face it; when you have chemistry with someone, you can usually sense it within the first 20 minutes. In one knowing glance or sly smile, you can tell that one kiss would transform her lip gloss into an electrical conductor. Now, just because there's a spark doesn't mean a relationship will work, but can a relationship work without the spark? Sure. We call that friendship.

The Cure for Line Disease

Any pickup lines that have actually worked on you?

—PAT, HOBOKEN, NEW JERSEY

A conversation with a man at a party once ended with him saying, "Hey, it's been nice talking with you. If you ever break up with your boyfriend, call me." My boyfriend was in the room, so I found his comment pretty bold—and I liked that. He told me his name and where he worked, and he walked away. Six months later, my relationship was over, and I was asking the receptionist for his extension.

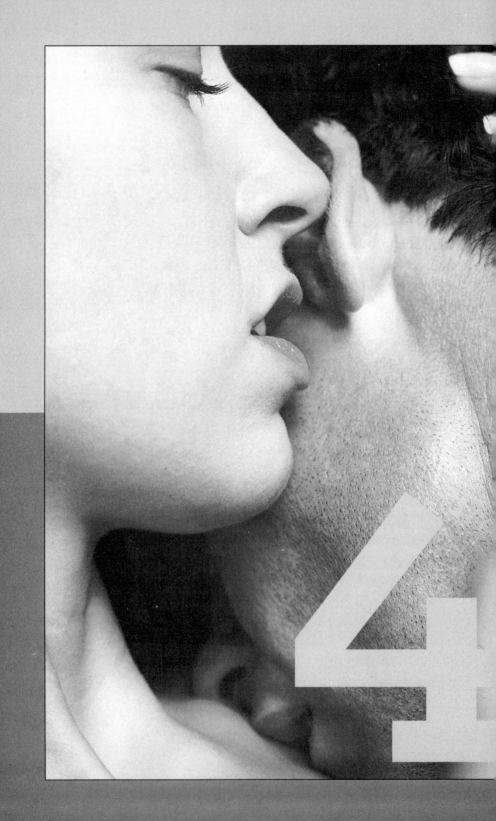

THE SEX FILES

When I say "bedroom," what comes to mind? Do you see a box spring, some sheets, and a comforter? Or do you see a domestic playground, a coed wrestling ring, a drop zone for all the dirty thoughts that come parachuting out of your head?

If your brain conjured anything like the latter, this is the section for you. Inside, you'll find instructions for the most knee-buckling, bone-rattling, so-hot-it-sets-off-the-fire-alarm sex of your life—the kind of stuff Serta execs forgot to consider when they put warranties on their mattresses.

Oh, and for those of you who saw only a bedroom? You, my friend, need this section even more. Prepare to expand your mind.

Touch Her Here

She's irresistible; now make her insatiable.
Learn the 6 unsung spots on a woman and how
to touch them, and prepare to enter her history
books under "Best Thing Ever to Happen to
My Body."   BY JENNIFER BENJAMIN

1. Nape of the neck

A nexus of nerve endings makes this one of the most sensitive parts of a woman's body, says Barbara Keesling, Ph.D.,
author of *The Good Girl's Guide to Bad Girl Sex*. Exhaling
while placing soft kisses along her hairline will get the rest
of her nerves standing on end.

2. Inner arm

The skin is very thin here, so the lightest touch can give
her goose bumps. Gently run your fingertips up and
down her inner forearm, New York City sexologist Logan
Levkoff suggests, and lightly stroke her wrist, a sensitive
pulse point.

3. Lower abdomen

Glide the back of your hand and knuckles across her lower
abs and down around her hip bones. "It's a mental turn-on
because she's wondering what's next," says Levkoff. "She'll
also have a physical response because the skin itself is highly
sensitive." She'll be begging you to head further south.

4. Lower back

You know that little slope at the base of her spine, right
above her butt? That indentation is very receptive to any

attention—especially delicate rubbing. "You want to massage the spot with a very gentle, circular motion," explains Keesling. "Remember that your goal isn't to get her muscle knots out, but to trigger a sexual response."

5. Back of the thigh

Right where cheek meets thigh is a crease with lots of nerve endings. These folds are partial to being licked, says Keesling, so slowly drag your tongue along each line and watch her convulse with pleasure.

6. Back of the knee

Nobody thinks to go there, "so when you stimulate it, she's, like, 'Whoa, where'd that come from?'" says Levkoff. Softly kiss or tickle the area (including the upper calf), but make sure she's lying down. Unless you think you can catch her when her legs give out.

The Dirty Dozen

12 questions designed to measure how much zing
you have in your schwing

BY SARAH MILLER

WOMEN ARE NUTCASES about magazine tests. Their part of the newsstand is an interrogation from emotional hell, with the covers shouting questions: "Is he ready to commit? Test on page 62," "Is his commitment for real? Test on page 107," "He's committed, but for how long? Test on page 309," and, finally, "Commitment: How do you spell it? Test on page 437."

Obviously, most of these tests have no relevance for guys. The only reason any of you would lift a finger to answer questions is if (a) your life depended on it, or (b) correct answers might lead to more sex. Which is why the editors of this book asked me to devise this sex test: They know that (b) is always your favorite answer.

This special precoital shakedown focuses on what it takes to get—and keep—a woman in bed. (And I, being a woman—with many female friends who complain, and lavish praise, without shame—should know. In fact, I'm in bed with a guy right now specifically because he answered questions 3, 4, 7 through 10, and 12 correctly.) Think of this as a specialized AP exam, only with French kissing instead of actual French.

SECTION 1

GETTING TO YES

1. You have treated the fascinating, gorgeous, and—most surprisingly—interested-in-you Elizabeth to several expensive meals. The most recent of these has just ended, and the two of you are now walking into your apartment. You are extremely ready for sex.

To ensure that it happens, you will now . . .

A. Light candles, put D'Angelo on the stereo, and ask Elizabeth to dance.

B. Invite Elizabeth into the bedroom.

C. Invite Elizabeth to join you while you watch the last half of *Baseball Tonight*, like you always do at this time.

D. Offer Elizabeth a drink—it gives you something to do, and also gives you courage for whatever comes next.

The answer is C. You've spent money and time on Elizabeth. You obviously like her and are interested in getting to know her, and vice versa. So why not simply incorporate her into your routine and let one thing—as it almost certainly will—lead to another? Keeping your post-date activities low-key lets her into your world and puts her at ease. This is in marked contrast to A and B, which are equally horrifying—nothing ruins the "We'll probably have sex" vibe like an introduction of the "We're definitely going to have sex" vibe. D makes us wonder if you're too chicken to do it sober, or if you would even bother.

2. Two years have passed, and you and Elizabeth are getting married in 2 weeks. Even though everything is all set, she's been so busy triple-checking with the caterers that she's forgotten why she's marrying you in the first place: to provide you with a lifetime of regular sex. You need to get some today. What's your plan of attack?

A. Offer to do items 12 and 13 on her to-do list, to get yourself onto it.

B. Book a luxury hotel room for one night.

C. Sit her down and explain to her that everything's set and she can just relax—preferably naked and covered with baby oil.

D. Make yourself as scarce as possible—home from work late, to the gym early. When women miss you, they want you.

The answer is A. It might look to you as if plans are going smoothly and therefore B and C are perfectly rational means of getting her mind off the wedding and onto your erect penis. What this doesn't take into account is that men are able to stay calm, cool, and collected only because women are so busy maintaining order in the world. Don't tell her there's nothing to worry about because you don't know anything about it. I'll bet you didn't even order your own tux, and if you did, I'll bet someone with a vagina was holding your hand the whole time. I'm not saying Elizabeth's not acting like a freak. She probably is. But she's your freak, and if you want to interest her in pleasing you, start out by pleasing her. (If you guessed D, it's a nice idea, but if the wedding's planned and she can't find you, she might just marry someone else.)

SECTION 2

FOREPLAY

3. True or false: The most important aspect of foreplay is oral sex.

False. We're glad the clitoris has, uh, risen to prominence in recent years. An unfortunate side effect of this phenomenon, however, is that men are almost too eager to go down on us. I mean, you've been making out with a guy for, like, 2 minutes, and all of a sudden he disappears under the sheets and you realize, God in heaven, he's going for it, already. Yes, women like oral sex. But it's all about warming her up with the kissing and then moving on to the next stages. Let us learn what your face looks like before showing us the top of your head.

4. As you know from reading your girlfriends' magazines—oh, jeez, not another quiz!—foreplay (which we now know means everything from kissing onward) is great. But there's a reason it's called fore-play: It's actually supposed to end at some point and result in just plain play. Match the sexual situation (on the left) with the number of minutes of foreplay (on the right) women will expect and appreciate.

1. Sex in a bathroom at a party	A. 3
2. Sex on the first date	B. 10
3. Sex on the third date	C. 45
4. Long-term-relationship sex	D. A bit more than 1
5. Sex with your ex	E. 30
6. Relationship sex at a parent's house	F. 20

1. D (Everyone's so drunk that it's about the experience, not the orgasms.)

2. C (If you're that hot for each other, you might as well enjoy, and prolong, the buildup.)

3. B (Maintain that bodice-ripping feeling of sexual tension being released.)

4. F (Put in some effort, but don't overdo it; we all know what we're here for by now.)

5. A (Get in and get out before one of you comes to your senses.)

6. E (The less actual intercourse, the less embarrassing/incriminating noise.)

5. Of all the Hollywood sex clichés, the one that women find most absurd is . . .

A. Women coming to orgasm in 2 minutes.

B. Women having sex standing up.

C. Young women having sex with older men.

D. All of the above.

The answer is B. We know that a real-time sex scene would take half the movie, so A is out. We also know that sometimes, to get a movie made, Michael Douglas or Michael Caine will be paired with someone much younger and prettier than he could ever get in real life. Oh, wait, that is real life! But we wonder if it's logistically possible for a woman to writhe in ecstasy while having intercourse on her feet. She's barely being penetrated. There's been no foreplay, and, finally, how does she concentrate on orgasm when she's busy hoping she doesn't sprain an ankle twisting out of her stilettos?

SECTION 3

TECHNIQUE

6. The key component of oral sex is . . .

A. Pressure.
B. Speed.
C. Motion.
D. None of the above.

The answer is D because the most important component of oral sex is your hands. You probably already use them to caress the rest of her body while you're busy down there, and that's fine. But you shouldn't hesitate to involve them in the main event. Use them on her clitoris when your tongue needs a break. Use them to stimulate her G-spot or to adjust her position for the most favorable possible access to the clitoris. You can give a woman an orgasm without your hands, but *with* them you can give her a much, much better one.

7. The second-most-important aspect of oral sex is . . .

A. Pressure.
B. Speed.
C. Motion.

The answer is A. Speed and motion are important, too; it's just that if you don't nail pressure first, you're lost. The clitoris is very persnickety. If you touch it too hard, it hurts; if you don't touch it hard enough, you might as well be licking her forehead. This means that your first oral sex experience with a woman may have to incorporate a Q & A session wherein the two of you establish what's working and what's not.

8. By and large, the sexual position most likely to encourage a woman to scream with pleasure is . . .

A. Man on top.
B. Doggy style.
C. Woman on top.

The answer is C. There's a lot of debate about whether women have G-spots and whether women who come during intercourse are actually just having their clitorises indirectly stimulated and so on. Until the debate is settled, the clitoris is your surest route. Woman on top—which allows for deep penetration and for your pubic bone to touch her clitoris—gives everyone what they're after.

9. Penis size: You've heard it doesn't matter. You've heard it's everything. What's the bottom line?

A. The bigger the better.
B. Women actually find big penises intimidating and prefer small ones.
C. Women are intimidated by large penises but underwhelmed by small ones. Medium is best.
D. All of the above.

The answer is D. A group of women—likely drunk women—discussing penis size would be divided in their preferences. Yes, there are some size queens, but for every one of them, there's a woman who's more turned on by a smaller penis. It may fit her better or allow for positions a larger one would not. In between, there's the whole medium camp. Think of penises like breasts. (Well, not exactly, of course, because you might have a nervous breakdown.) They are body parts about which we've been taught to equate bigger with better, but tastes run the gamut.

SECTION 4

MISCUES

10. In general, you've found your sexual machinery to be both robust and dependable. Lately, however, like a little soft baby, it seems to be napping. You wouldn't be that concerned, except that you have just started dating Someone New, and she has no way of knowing whether this is business as usual. What should you do?

> **A.** Assure her that this doesn't happen often and try to forget about it.
>
> **B.** Assure her that this doesn't happen often, shower her with praise, and show her some literature on the benign nature of occasional failure to perform.
>
> **C.** Say nothing, and keep your relationship above the waist until further notice.
>
> **D.** If this doesn't happen often, maybe you're just not hot for this woman. Break it off.

The answer is A. By the time women have been having sex for a couple of years, we've seen this happen a lot, especially at the beginning of relationships, when you might be a little nervous. We might even find it a little cute. We do want you to acknowledge it, so C isn't a good idea—unless, of course, you want us to wonder if it's our fault. Naturally, we can't prevent you from jumping to conclusions (D), and there's a chance that that's what's going on, sure, but there's a much better chance it's not. B will scare us, so that by the time your little man is up and running, your woman will already be gone.

10a. True or false: If your machinery is working fine but firing too soon, you should follow the same course of action as above.

True. Women are actually pretty understanding about this sort of thing, especially if it's not a habit, and especially if you don't whine about it—which is, naturally, much more unpleasant and embarrassing than the actual problem itself. As long as everybody reaches the destination, the journey is worth it. If you get there first, go back and give her a lift with any of the myriad methods at your disposal.

11. What should you do if you really don't like giving women oral sex?

> **A.** Simply tell your girlfriends that it's not in your repertoire, become extremely good with your hands, and try not to date former lesbians.
> **B.** Perform oral sex only on request.
> **C.** Pretend you like it and do it a lot to prove this.
> **D.** Just don't go there. Your preferences are your preferences, and no amount of chatter will change that.

I'm going to level with you. If cunnilingus were part of my job description, I would be a little frightened. I mean, golly, it's a jungle in there! However, as much as I would love to tell you that B is a viable option, I just can't. And as for C, well, receiving oral sex from a man who is clearly miserable performing it is like using an egg salad sandwich as an emery board. There's something about your willingness to put your mouth on this special, special place that's sort of essential to our having any respect for you. That strikes out D and leaves you with only A, which won't win you any friends and won't earn you the oral stim *you're* probably looking for. So if it's a "cleanliness" thing, head for the showers and take her with you. Rub-a-dub-dub. If it's a mental block, put your brain up on the rack at the sex counselor's body shop and see if you can work through this.

SECTION 5

AFTERGLOW AND AFTER

12. You become very tired after sex. How many months do you have to have sex with a woman before you can simply orgasm, say, "God, that was great," and pass out?

A. 6 months.

B. Give it a full year.

C. I need more information.

D. Forget it.

The answer is C. There are two reasons women like to talk to men after they have sex with them. The first is that women really have a great deal of curiosity about your childhood, your feelings, and so on. The second is that after sharing themselves with you on this intimate level, they need affirmation of your attachment to them.

If you've been dating a woman, you talk daily, and she's confident of your interest in her, start postcoital snoring after about 3 months. At this point she's heard enough, and after sex she'd much rather watch *CSI* than hear about how beautiful you think she is or how your dad doesn't really love you.

However, if you're involved in some on-again, off-again sex thing totally dependent on your whims, she's going to be desperate to connect with you after the sex. And for as long as this goes on—be it a month or years—you're going to have to earn your keep with some emotional late-night confessions. Kind of makes you rethink that whole commitment thing, eh?

SCORING

Give yourself 10 points for each correct answer.

90–130: You are a chairman of the headboard. Where her pleasure stops and yours begins is a fuzzy, ecstatic place.

50–80: Your performance is spottier than week-old sheets. You need to extend your focus beyond the length of your penis.

0–40: Until you increase your understanding of her needs, yours will never be met. Seek remedial sex sessions with an understanding partner.

Baggage Check

A woman brings more than lingerie into the bedroom.
She brings her exes, her hang-ups, and other carry-ons
that can get in your way

BY TED SPIKER

WHEN A GUY PACKS for a long weekend, he shoves some boxers and Right Guard into a gym bag. A woman? She packs a cosmetic case, a small suitcase, a garment bag, her favorite pillow, a purse, and a shopping bag or two.

Same with sexual baggage. The stuff a woman lugs around—from how her ex treated her to how she feels about her body—could put a skycap on disability. Trouble is, men aren't x-ray machines able to see every emotional burden a woman brings to bed (so we recommend frequent strip searches). This lack of knowledge translates into infrequent sex, stagnant sex, or no sex.

To help, we've examined her shipping manifest and come up with a plan to lighten the load so both of you can enjoy the trip. Start unpacking tonight.

PROBLEM: SHE'S NOT REACHING ORGASM

THE BAGGAGE

HER EX. "Trust is the number one issue," says Ava Cadell, Ph.D., Ed.D., a sex therapist and the author of *12 Steps to Everlasting Love*. "If a previous partner was unfaithful or deceitful, that's a biggie. A woman cannot have an orgasm if she cannot surrender to her partner."

GUILT. Many women have only one way they can climax, and they'd rather not tell you how they discovered it—maybe with a former boyfriend or, egads, from masturbating. "Maybe she can come only if she has her legs closed and is on her side. It seems too weird to tell you, but that's the truth," says Pepper Schwartz, Ph.D., a marriage therapist and the author of *Everything You Know about Love and Sex Is Wrong.*

UNPACK IT

Stop talking about it. Saying the words "orgasm" and "Are you finished?" is like asking her to have sex in front of 20,000 people at the Staples Center—too much pressure. Tell her you just want to enjoy the experience—your enthusiasm will help more than any technique, says Cadell. Some emotion and appreciation ("You know exactly what to do"; "I want this to last all night. . . . ") will relax and excite her.

MAKE SUBTLE CHANGES. If she climaxes only in one position or by one method, change where you have sex, but not what you do. "The floor feels different from the bed; the couch feels different from the floor," says Lou Paget, a sex educator in Los Angeles and the author of *365 Days of Sensational Sex.*

DRAW IT OUT. With oral sex—a reliable route—think of her body as a treasure map. Don't just dig; explore first. Kiss her cheek, neck, arms, and so on, until you reach the spot. Even then, take a detour to her thighs and her knees. "You want to drive her nuts so she begs you to lick her," Cadell says. Then start by gently kissing, and gradually add circular motions with a little bit of pressure.

PROBLEM: SHE'S INHIBITED

THE BAGGAGE

HER UPBRINGING. She hears voices: *You're a slut. You're sleazy.* "Men don't get these messages. Women started getting them when they were 9," Paget says. Your girlfriend hears everyone from her parents to her pastor. "There are those who feel God doesn't want people to have sex for pleasure; there are a lot of people who feel oral sex is a sin," says Gloria Brame, Ph.D., a licensed clinical sexologist. The theme: Sex without procreating is bad. Sex before marriage is worse. Sex with whipped cream will fast-forward you to hell.

HER INEXPERIENCE. If she suspects—or knows—that you've had more experience, she could become more conservative than the *O'Reilly Factor,* for fear that she's not doing something right, Schwartz says.

UNPACK IT

PLAY NAKED BOGGLE. Make sure nudity isn't always associated with sex. "Nothing reduces inhibitions like laughing and sharing a joke when you're naked," Brame says. Your mate will be comfortable and more creative. Cadell suggests this trick: Take a shower together, but put powdered Jell-O in the showerhead. When you turn it on, flavored slime comes out. It's fun, it's sticky, and it's sexy without the sex.

COMPROMISE. Indulge your fantasies without making her uncomfortable. Cadell remembers one client who took his wife to a strip club, and a dancer gave them a lap dance together. "His wife loved it," Cadell says. "It was a way to make a threesome without the sex, and then they went home and had the best sex they ever had." Too racy? Try adjoining massages—woman touching you, man touching her.

TEASE HER. "The way to break down the barrier is to make her feel cute and sexy, make her blush a little bit," she says. "A tense body is physically cold. Blushing is warm. Get her blood circulating." Brame suggests playful teasing, like pillow fights, touching, or light tickling, as foreplay.

PROBLEM: SHE'S A RULE MAKER

THE BAGGAGE

HER BODY IMAGE. She feels too fat or too flat: Lights stay off; clothes stay on. Body-image issues aren't as much about specific body parts as they are about general self-esteem and self-confidence, Brame says.

HER IGNORANCE. If she imposes a no-fly zone south of the belly, it could mean she hasn't visited there much herself. "Men have to handle themselves every day," Brame says. "It's quite possible for a woman to go through life without touching herself directly."

UNPACK IT

FOCUS ON HER TRIGGER SPOTS. If she's self-conscious about her butt, take extra time there. Ignoring it actually reinforces her feelings, says Cadell. "Taking time is going to make her feel loved and sexually empowered," she says. Tell her how much you love her butt or her breasts, and persist. She needs to hear it a lot before she buys it, Schwartz says.

SHOW HER OFF. She's heard your compliments. Now call in reinforcements—other men. Nothing kinky. Just go to a bar, lean in, tell her she's sexy, and then mention how that guy by the wall has been checking her out. Sometimes a boost in body confidence (and sexual arousal) comes when the nonverbal compliments come from someone else.

PROBLEM: SHE RARELY WANTS IT

THE BAGGAGE

HER "OTHER" ISSUES. You want it five times a week; she'd be happy with once a month. Brame says that in her experience as a therapist, she's learned there's often no obvious reason for not wanting sex. Instead, the reasons have little to do with sex—your wife is unhappy about money problems, parenting, communication. The problem is how close she feels to you in nonsexual ways.

UNPACK IT

MAKE A LIST. After your next fight, suggest that you both make a list of the five things you've recently had fights about. Then prioritize the issues so it's clear what needs to be worked on. "It helps you stop making sex the scapegoat and lets you work on the really big issues," Brame says.

BRING IN THE HEAVY ARTILLERY. "For women, sex drive can be enhanced with romance," says Helen Fisher, Ph.D., an anthropologist at Rutgers University and the author of *The First Sex*. "It's amazing how you eliminate the sexual baggage when you're deeply attached." What's your makeup tactic—flowers, card, tickets to dirt-track racing? Try using it before you screw up. A woman's sex drive increases when you do something nice—and unexpected.

Disorder in the Courtship

Sentenced to life without her? Here's how to successfully
appeal her verdict. Please rise

BY NICOLE BELAND

EVEN WOMEN WHO PAY NO MIND to relationship rules give
devout reverence to the most golden of all: Never get back with an ex.
This has been my only heart-healthy maxim since high school, when
one of my first boyfriends cheated, groveled his way back, and
cheated a second time. I vowed it'd never happen again.

A decade later, I broke my own decree. After 3 years of dating
and a nasty fight that left us storming down the street in different di-
rections, my ex and I weren't speaking at all. Then came a letter in
the mail. Then another. Then a third, all saying things so sincere and
surprising I couldn't help thinking things would be different. So I
caved, and fell hopefully back into his arms.

And if I did, your former girlfriend probably will, too. It will help
your case immensely if you say all the right words and if you look hot
begging for mercy. But most of all, "she's going to need cold, hard evidence that whatever went wrong is going to change," says Jackie
Black, Ph.D., a psychologist and certified relationship coach in Los
Angeles. If you have the determination, we have the moves that will
put you and your ex on the road to sweet reconciliation.

HER FINAL WORDS: "If you can't make a commitment, it's over!"
Facing an ultimatum, you reacted by refusing to be bullied.

Are You Sure You Want Her Back?

Perhaps you've been there: You pine incessantly over an ex, get back together, then promptly, desperately want to break it off again. Before you launch a comeback effort, ask yourself two questions, says John DeLamater, Ph.D., a professor of sociology at the University of Wisconsin. First, for this relationship to work, would one of you have to change a major personality trait? "The truth is, it's usually easier to change the relationship than to change a person," says DeLamater. Second, are you positive it's her you want back, or do you just miss having a girlfriend? To answer, make a list of her qualities that you'd be hard-pressed to find in another woman. The longer the list, the more motivated you'll be. Only three items? Forget her.

Good for you. Except now you're thinking that getting more serious isn't such a bad idea. "Most guys are more content in a committed relationship than they thought they'd be," says Drew Pinsky, M.D., cohost of the radio show *Loveline* and author of *Cracked: Putting Broken Lives Together Again*. Does she make you happy? Share your values? Have similar goals? Three yeses, and she's probably right that you should move forward.

WHAT TO SAY: Tell her she was right to dump you. Hearing that you understand her point of view will soften her up. "Then announce a deadline by which you'll act," says Dr. Pinsky. (Only don't call it a deadline.) Promise that within 6 months—any longer will seem like stalling—she'll be either sharing the same pad or sporting a diamond, whichever applies.

WHAT TO DO: Be enthusiastic and proactive about the annoying logistics of your promise. Rent a moving van or start researching honeymoons. Voluntary participation is the only way you'll get her to take you seriously.

HER FINAL WORDS: "You're emotionally unavailable."

I've dumped a man for this reason myself. I also accused him of being "closed off," "insensitive," and "distant." Of course, the poor guy didn't know what I was talking about. Surprisingly, neither did I. "Women frequently use psychological catchphrases without really knowing what they mean," says Black. "What she should be saying is that she needs you to talk about and show your feelings more." Which isn't so hard once you get the hang of it.

WHAT TO SAY: Write a letter containing all the mushy stuff you've never said before—like how no woman has ever made you as happy, excited, or in love. "Explain that there's nothing you want more than to be emotionally close to her, but you need her help," says Black. Then ask her what specifically would make her feel closer to you. She'll understand how hard it was for you to spill your guts, which will melt her heart. Repeat as necessary.

WHAT TO DO: Start explaining your actions in terms of the feelings behind them. So, instead of "Can we talk about this later?" say, "It's been an emotionally draining day. What I really feel like doing is just being with you and relaxing."

HER FINAL WORDS: "I need space."

You thought asking her out six nights in a row was romantic. But your full-court press freaked her out. "Some guys show their cards too early," says Dr. Pinsky. "Then his girlfriend worries he'll be too dependent on her for happiness." Yes, I know women are always complaining that guys don't fawn over them enough. But even though we crave sap, we value independence (ours and yours) just as much.

WHAT TO SAY: Send her an e-mail explaining that you understand how space would be good, that maybe things were moving too fast, that you, too, could use time to get your life back in balance. "Mention a trip you've been thinking of taking or a project that you've been wanting to throw yourself into," says Dr. Pinsky. "Suggest that she give you a call if she wants to spend some time together in the future."

WHAT TO DO: Put her out of your mind and make a plan to tackle a new project at work, climb Mount Kilimanjaro, train for a 10-K, whatever. If she finally does call, you'll be too busy to focus all of your time and energy on her—which she'll be sure to find irresistible.

HER FINAL WORDS: "I could never trust you again, slimeball!"

Getting caught being unfaithful, or on the brink of it, is the deepest relationship doo-doo a man can step in. Serious groveling is in order. "The more unusual the circumstances surrounding your slip, the more likely you'll be forgiven," says John DeLamater, Ph.D., a professor of sociology at the University of Wisconsin.

In other words, you're going to need one hell of a good explanation.

WHAT TO SAY: She probably won't take your call, so spill your guts to her voice mail. "Describe how you got into the strange situation," says DeLamater. Maybe the other woman was a flirtatious colleague or client whom you felt obligated to flirt back with to avoid offending. Or maybe you were reacting to some jealousy you were feeling because of a guy in your girlfriend's life. "Then let her know you realize you were a total jerk to do anything that could jeopardize the amazing relationship you have with her," says Black.

WHAT TO DO: Eliminate the other woman from your life. "If it was your secretary, find a way to get her reassigned," says DeLamater. "If it was a female friend, promise never to see her again." Messed around on a business trip? Tell your girlfriend that from now on, she's invited to go along.

HER FINAL WORDS: "You're not putting enough energy into the relationship."

When my friend Steve got dumped, he didn't know what hit

him. "Everything was fine; then suddenly she says I don't act as if I love her," he told me. This is common. Since you've already swapped plenty of "I love you's" and cuddled for hours after sex on dozens of Sundays, it's obvious to you how much you care about each other. So obvious, in fact, that all the little stuff that means a lot to her—holding hands, calling just to say hello—barely feels necessary anymore.

WHAT TO SAY: Show up on her doorstep and apologize for failing to realize how unappreciated she was feeling, says Black. Tell her that you want to do more; you just want to make sure you're doing the things that matter most to her. Ask for specifics.

WHAT TO DO: Sacrifice something that's been taking time and energy away from the relationship. If you work late all week, force yourself to leave the office at 6 P.M. 2 days a week and plan something with her on those nights, even if it simply means picking up a DVD and ordering takeout. Don't skimp on physical affection. "Kiss her first thing in the morning, last thing at night, and at random moments for no reason," says Black.

HER FINAL WORDS: "He's flying me to Paris on his private jet." Um . . . cheer up, bud—you're better off without her.

Unleash Her Inner Beast

There are some things a man will never change about
a woman. But he can use these sneaky strategies to make
the best of her worst traits

BY SARAH MILLER

SURE, WOMEN CAN BE FICKLE, but there are certain things
you can rely on. We are much prettier than you are. We smell great,
even on Saturday. If we find ourselves at a baby shower, we generally
don't pass the time scouting out a quiet corner to shotgun a beer.
Sadly, you can also rely on this: There are certain things we say and
do that drive you out of your mind and that we have no inclination,
or ability, to give up.

It sounds a lot worse than it is. Just because we cling to our personal brand of insanity as if it were a black cashmere cardigan, in our
size, with a cunning little packet of extra buttons, on sale at Saks, you
don't always have to respond by futilely wrestling back. Our behavior
will never change.

So, the only thing left to do is to change your reaction to it.
You'll be surprised how well it works, how little it hurts, and how
much of your precious lifestyle stays fully intact.

**1. We will never stop trying to get you to tell us how
you feel.**

WHY: You have feelings sometimes. And mostly you feel like
keeping them to yourself. Women, however, believe that all feelings—
from tiny good ones ("Oh my God, I put the perfect amount of sugar
in my coffee today!") to big, bad ones ("Sometimes I hate myself")—

Facts of Life

46
Percentage of men's fantasies
that involve their partner,
compared with 64 percent of
women's —*JOURNAL OF SEX RESEARCH*

deserve to make the miraculous journey from our mouths to your ears. We yearn for a similar emotional play-by-play from you.

WHAT YOU'VE BEEN DOING: Naturally, you've looked deep into your soul for the words to describe your thoughts, feelings, and ideas. You've tried to string them all together with as much believable filler as possible, hoping that your true feelings—frustration that you're not in bed, enjoying a Manhattan and *Conan O'Brien*—aren't too apparent.

WHAT YOU SHOULD DO: Chances are, if you're engaged in the process of "becoming more emotionally communicative," you've allowed this to take up a lot of space in the relationship. It's time to introduce a new concept entirely: Men should probably share their feelings a little more, but women need to share theirs less. The truth is, we're totally jealous of your stiff upper lips. We're embarrassed about our compulsion to run off to Camp Introspection with you, our friends, or perfect strangers. Take advantage of this. Next time she begs you to emote, instead of responding with guilt and a promise to open a vein and/or tear duct, say, "I think I'm just more comfortable weighing things in my own head than you are. Maybe I need less validation." She'll start to panic that there's something wrong with her. And because of the very nature of what she's panicking about, she'll do it quietly. Which means less chatter during *Conan*.

2. We will never stop freaking out if you don't call us the day after we have sex with you for the first time.

WHY: When it comes to sex, it's not customary for you to wrestle with mixed feelings. You got laid, and if there's a downside to this, it's entirely unclear what it could be. For women, however, the postsex meltdown is as crucial to the experience as the sex itself. A woman's number one fear is being labeled a slut, and your prompt follow-up phone call is the event that will prove to her that she's not.

WHAT YOU'VE BEEN DOING: Sometimes you call—even if it's nerve-racking and not enjoyable. Sometimes you don't, which is not much fun for you either, thanks to the vague feeling of shame and confusion that gnaws at you all day long.

WHAT YOU SHOULD DO: E-mail a message of no fewer than three and no more than six sentences. If you write something really romantic or dirty (cute dirty, not dirty dirty—"Thinking of you and that cute pink thong," say, as opposed to "Thinking of you and what's under your pink thong"), one sentence is sufficient. You can be blissfully evasive and properly respectful all at once. One of those rare opportunities in life when so little effort from you results in so much satisfaction for her.

3. We will never stop trying to change your appearance.

WHY: Your girlfriend likes you, but not nearly as much as she likes the image of what you would become if you'd sport the haircut, pants, and shoes of her choice. Furthermore, a small part of her seriously believes that in agreeing to be your girlfriend, she has earned a debt of gratitude you can repay only by becoming a human sacrifice at the Temple of the Eternal Makeover.

WHAT YOU'VE BEEN DOING: Struggling to maintain individuality and control by refusing her advice. If the $7 barber and basic black shoes were good enough for your father and grandfather (and your mother and grandmother), they should be plenty good enough for you (and her), too.

WHAT YOU SHOULD DO: Start listening, and then start cleaning out your closet. Women are especially good at knowing which T-shirts look good on you and which ones make you look dumpy, too skinny, or too fat. A good way to approach letting her into your sartorial life is to go through your closet together and decide what's allowed to stay and what's going to that great Salvation Army in the sky. Next up: a strategic strike at the menswear shop.

Please don't let this experience make you question your independence or manhood. Allowing your girlfriend to take control of your wardrobe is a brilliant tactical move with handsome rewards. She, operating on the very mistaken assumption that you care about clothes as much as she does, will subsequently assume that she now owes you decision-making power in areas that are way more important. So you might be wearing what she wants, but you won't even notice because you'll be eating the food you like, watching the movies you like, and spending Saturdays playing paintball instead of wandering around Bed Bath & Beyond, looking for periwinkle toilet seat covers.

4. We will never stop demanding that you talk to us the second you walk in the door.

WHY: Both men and women have long days filled with annoying people, unfortunate accidents, and frustrating problems. The difference is that you rush home to forget this, while we rush home to discuss it.

WHAT YOU'VE BEEN DOING: Trying to focus on our fascinating, detailed story of office betrayal. But you're so exhausted and in need of a mental vacation that you can't stop looking in the fridge, at the TV, and at the sports page, thereby failing miserably to listen to us and incurring our wrath.

WHAT YOU SHOULD DO: If you don't feel like talking to us at the end of the day, you have only one option. Hide. Go to a bar, drive to a park and sit on a swing, park your car a block from home and sit there staring into space. Don't even try coming home and saying, "I need a little time to myself right now," because if a woman can see you, she figures you're fair game for conversation.

5. We will never stop hounding you with the question "Did you ask your boss for time off yet?"

WHY: To us, "Let's go on vacation" means "Let's book the thing tomorrow." To you, it means "Yes, I'd like to go on vacation . . . theoretically . . . when conditions in my career are totally perfect and I won't get in trouble for being away." This question really means "Did you grow some balls today?"

WHAT YOU'VE BEEN DOING: Avoiding asking your boss, and avoiding answering us by giving us reasons that you're waiting for the right time to ask.

WHAT YOU SHOULD DO: Men work too hard. And if you don't believe me, try counting on just one hand the number of them you know who've died of heart attacks. The next time your girlfriend/wife says she wants to go on vacation, ask yourself, realistically, when you can take off a few days or a week in the next 3 months. (If you can't, you might be in the wrong job.) Ask your boss for the time. Then go on vacation, like a normal person.

6. We will never stop expecting you to change our tires, replace fuses, or program the VCR.

WHY: All our lives, people have told us that we aren't good at mechanical things or math. A small percentage of us declared this notion sexist and went out and learned calculus and bought toolboxes. But

---

INSTANT SEXPERT

How Can I Last Longer in Bed?

The average guy lasts 14 minutes during intercourse. Not bad, considering that the average guy with premature ejaculation holds out for only 24 seconds. To increase your staying power, masturbate an hour or two before your rendezvous. It may cost you some immediate passion, but it'll help slow the pace at which you become aroused and the speed of your climax. Using a circular thrusting motion and frequently changing positions will also help you hold out.

most of us just said, "Fine, that stuff is totally boring anyway. We'll be at the pool."

WHAT YOU'VE BEEN DOING: Programming the VCR, changing our tires, doing our income taxes, cleaning our pool. Thinking, at times angrily, Jeez, a monkey, even a girl monkey, could do this.

WHAT YOU SHOULD DO: Next time you start to feel like a put-upon hired hand, remind yourself that there are benefits to hoarding knowledge. The less we know about hardware, the more you seem like a genius for understanding it. More important, even if you did school us in basic mechanics, we'd always assume we were doing it wrong and ask lots of questions far more annoying than the job itself.

7. We will never stop being obsessed with our weight.

WHY: As you know, there is a great deal of societal pressure on women to be thin. It's also a lot easier to try to become thinner than it is to become funnier or smarter or get an entirely new face, so you can see why dieting's such an appealing hobby.

WHAT YOU'VE BEEN DOING: Responding to the endless stream of weight-focused anxiety with "No, you look the same as always" and then thinking to yourself, . . . except a little more like Shamu.

WHAT YOU SHOULD DO: Though we will never stop bitching about our weight, we might just stop bitching about it to you. Especially if you say something like "I am sorry that you feel fat. As you can see, I haven't left you yet, so you can't be too terribly hideous. In the meantime, you should either take the necessary steps to remove that weight or never ever mention it to me again, lest I die of utter boredom." Then buy her a treadmill and tell her she's not allowed to talk until she actually believes she's thin.

Bring Out Her Wild Side

Your fantasy woman—a reckless babe with a lustful mind—
just might be the one you're with. Here's how to set her loose

BY CAROLINE TIGER

SO YOU'RE INVOLVED with a classy lady, the kind you're proud to show off to your parents. Guess what. She might be a naughty superfreak on the inside—it's up to you to coax that out of her. The key: Tell her it's okay.

"Women are conditioned to fulfill the role of 'good girl,'" says Judith Schervren, Ph.D., coauthor of *Be Loved for Who You Really Are*. "They need permission from you to break that mold, to change from being their parents' good girl to your hot girlfriend." Here's how.

SHOW HER OFF. If you tell her she's the sexiest one in the room, it will embolden her. "Whisper in her ear how much she turns you on, and combine that with some public neck kissing and hand-holding," says Ian Kerner, author of *She Comes First*. "Find semiprivate places— a coatroom or an empty room at a party—where you can touch her." Get her used to that and she'll start to equate public places with sexual thoughts. And in private, she'll reciprocate—eagerly.

INDULGE HER FANTASIES. If she's expressed an interest in sky-diving, book the plane. If she's joked about skinny-dipping, she wants you to find a lake. "If you challenge her to overcome her fears and you do it with her, it'll build trust and make her more likely to go out on a limb the next time," says Yvonne Fulbright, author of *The Hot Guide to Safer Sex*. The safer she feels with you, the more daring she'll feel she can be.

CRACK UP WITH HER. "Make sure you laugh with her when she does something funny or outrageous or silly," says Schervren. The more scandalous she gets, the more you should encourage her. Imagine her doing something wild; then describe it to her. "You have to see her that way before she'll be able to act that way," says Schervren. "She has to feel confident that you think she's capable of it."

TEASE HER ALL DAY. Don't start seducing her at bedtime. Start the process with a long kiss in the A.M., and tell her you can't wait to get your hands on her later. "Knowing you find her irresistible is the ultimate turn-on," says Regena Thomashauer, author of *Mama Gena's Marriage Manual.* "The thought of it will keep her turned on all day." Follow up with e-mails or phone calls—chances for her to express her wild side safely, without embarrassment—and you'll both be counting the hours.

QUICKIES

LOVE HER TWO TIMES

The new buzzword in the bedroom is "bigasm," a type of stimulation that may help you give her more intense orgasms. A woman must be simultaneously stimulated in two major erogenous zones—the clitoris and the G-spot—to better reach her orgasmic potential, says Ava Cadell, Ph.D., Ed.D., a sex therapist and the author of *12 Steps to Everlasting Love*. There are several techniques, but in a study of 12 couples, what follows was the scream-out-loud favorite: With your partner straddling you, invite her to tilt her pelvis so that her clitoris can rub against the shaft of your penis while the tip hits her G-spot. "The result is one of the most intense full-body orgasms," says Cadell.

PLASTIC NOT SO FANTASTIC

When choosing condoms, there's more to consider than ribbed versus mesh. According to new research from Family Health International, latex condoms are better than polyurethane at preventing pregnancy. After a 6-month study of more than 900 monogamous couples, researchers found that the pregnancy rate for those using polyurethane condoms was 9 percent, compared with only 5.4 percent for the couples copulating with latex. "Both the breakage and slippage rates were higher for the polyurethane group," says Markus Steiner, Ph.D., the lead study author. If you or your partner is allergic to latex, you might want to consider other forms of birth control.

SEX FOR THE SENSES

Hit These 5 Targets and Win a Prize—Her

You know that putting Tab A into Slot B won't make you a pro in the sack. Luckily, you have more than one tool at hand. "Bring all her senses into the experience," says Patti Britton, Ph.D., author of *The Complete Idiot's Guide to Sensual Massage.* "You'll enhance her pleasure, giving her what could be the best sex of her life." Don't you want to be responsible for that?

TASTE. Feeding Kim Basinger was one of the few smart career moves Mickey Rourke made, so imitate it. Serve up exotic fruits like kiwis, pomegranates, or star fruits in bed. "Rare tastes are psychologically arousing for her because they seem almost forbidden," says Olivia St. Claire, author of *302 Advanced Techniques for Driving a Man Wild in Bed.* And henceforth the produce aisle will turn her on.

HEARING. Chris Berman's blathering is not an aphrodisiac. Pick up a nature CD or a sound machine. "Soothing noises enable her to get out of her own head and fully enjoy the moment," says Britton. If she's worried the kids will hear, put the noise machine in their room.

SMELL. The nose is connected to the limbic system of the brain, which controls libido. So certain scents—rose, jasmine, and ylang-ylang—can trigger sexual arousal. Put a couple of drops of scented oil (available at health food stores) on the lightbulb in your bedside lamp, switch it on, and watch her get turned on.

SIGHT. "Women respond to strength because it makes them feel more feminine," says St. Claire. "Any activity that involves muscle flexing and heavy lifting will demonstrate that you can take care of her, which is a major turn-on." Strap on a tool belt and do some home improvement. Or, before bed, do some pushups or pullups so your arms look more cut, enhancing your large-and-in-charge vibe.

TOUCH. Rub her from head to toe with massage oil—it's erotic because the slippery sensation mimics sex, explains St. Claire. Feeling more frisky but less messy? With a washable pen, write on each of her body parts exactly what you plan to do to it. Then follow through.

THE "YOU CAN CHILL" PILL

Broken condom got you tearing hair out of your head with worry? Get a prescription for the emergency contraceptive pill. Anybody can get an ECP prescription, even those of us without uteruses. If she agrees to take it within 72 hours of sex and pops a second pill 12 hours later, the FDA says you two will have an 89 percent chance of avoiding parenthood. According to the doctors we consulted, the best is levonorgestrel, marketed as Plan B. Essentially, it's a large dose of a synthetic hormone similar to progesterone. "It prevents the pregnancy by making the uterine environment hostile to implantation of a potentially fertilized ovum or by inhibiting ovulation altogether," says Robert Berg, M.D., a New York City gynecologist. (So, technically, your sperm may have hit pay dirt, but if the egg can't implant, it won't later require braces or college tuition.)

In Alaska, California, New Mexico, and Washington, Plan B is sold over the counter—as long as a pharmacist is willing to hand it over to you. Elsewhere, it's a prescription drug, so talk it over with your doctor. And no, it's not an alternative to the Pill. "There are still side effects due to the higher dose of hormones," says Dr. Berg, "so you would not want to take this every day as regular birth control. It's emergency contraception."

ASK THE GIRL NEXT DOOR

The honest truth about women from our lovely neighbor

Mouthwatering Thoughts

Do women fantasize about oral sex (giving and receiving) as much as men do? —WALTER, ST. LOUIS

I have many female friends with dirty minds, and they often focus their imaginations on oral sex. But I have a feeling their fantasies don't even come close to what the male brain is capable of. As for the giving/receiving part of your question, my informal survey of friends reveals that ladies would rather imagine themselves at the mercy of a talented tongue than showing off how well they can use their own. One of their most popular fantasies involves a large walnut desk with just enough legroom underneath to fit Russell Crowe.

Heel, Boy

Do women like having sex doggy style? —BENNY, VIA E-MAIL

Yes, we like it. A lot of women love it. But unless you're dating a woman who likes to refer to herself as your bitch, I wouldn't advise calling it "doggy style." If you absolutely have to describe it, call it having sex "from behind." It can be very stimulating to her G-spot, if she's into that. Your best option for repeat performances is not to call it anything. Just do it.

Wrap Enthusiast

What kind of condom do women prefer? —MIKE, ST. LOUIS

We're fans of lubricated latex condoms of reputable brands like Trojan, Durex, and LifeStyles. (Unless you're allergic to latex, please refrain from bringing any lamb innards to bed.) A snug fit is important—baggy rubbers have all the sensuality of plastic bags—so buy the size that fits your johnson, not your ego. (You can order sized-to-your-penis They-Fit condoms at condomania.com.) As for special effects, textured and ribbed can be very nice (but don't guarantee anything). A reservoir tip is important to prevent spillage. And mint-flavored can be pleasant if you're into practicing safe oral sex. Think colored condoms are funny? So will she. But think about it: Is that what you really want, a funny penis?

Foil the Mood

When and how can a guy bring up condoms without breaking the mood?   —MIKE, CHICAGO

There shouldn't be a discussion about condoms: You should just have one with you and put it on when you find yourself buck naked with a woman who's smiling at you from between her knees. If you find yourself lacking a prophylactic at the crucial moment, ask if she has one on hand. No need to be shy—women love it when a guy does the right thing without having to be asked.

Hot and Heavy Reading

You've said that you'd like a man who spends as much time reading about women's bodies as he does about sports and stocks. Any recommendations?   —JOE Q., VIA E-MAIL

I recently lent a friend my copy of *The Guide to Getting It On* by Paul Joannides, and I'm already sorry. It's blissfully devoid of B.S. and includes very specific how-tos. It also has hilarious comic-book-style illustrations that'd never get past the censors at Wal-Mart. If your goal is to help her have an orgasm, or more orgasms, another good option is Kim Cattrall's *Satisfaction*. The *Sex and the City* star had trouble climaxing until she discovered the techniques she describes. The instructions are detailed, but the tame language and illustrations make it an excellent choice for couples.

TO HAVE AND TO HOLD

G uys like comfort. That's one reason why, eventually, most of us quit foraging for the next new girl and settle down with a perennial partner. Living hand to mouth can be exciting (especially if that hand is at-tached to a 5-foot-9 brunette with a Britney Spears belly and a degree from Pole Dance U.), but nothing relaxes a guy like home-grown companionship.

Of course, stability doesn't mean every night as a couple will be a lovefest. There's going to be confusion. There are going to be fights. And there may even come a time when those old hunter-and-gatherer urges drive one of you—maybe even her—to abandon the safety of home for the great big wild.

To keep your relationship prosperous year after year, you may need some tips. And, wouldn't you know it, the chapters ahead will help you. Turn the page.

30 Secrets Every Woman Keeps from Her Man

All her naked, sexy (and a little scary) truths revealed

BY KATHRYN EISMAN

1. My best friend knows everything. She knows all of your vitals—from the size of your bank account to the size of your other, um, holdings—and she knows how both compare with those of every other man I've ever dated. I have done a hand-comparison measurement so I can divulge size and girth with a high level of accuracy. When my friend smirks at you knowingly, you are not imagining it. She knows. So just know that she knows, and deal with it. (It's not going to change.) Ask her about me, or chat with her about our relationship, at your own risk. She will tell me. Even—in fact especially—if she promises not to. This is not always a bad thing (for example, if you happen to be telling her how much you love me). But in general, re-member that she is my confidante first, and yours never.

2. Just looking at your hands can turn me on.

3. When you go away, even for a day, I sleep in your fa-vorite old T-shirt because it smells like you.

4. I'll never tell you exactly how many men I've slept with. No matter how sincere I appeared when I answered your question, chances are I wasn't. As an unscientific guideline, when a woman says she's slept with four men, the real number is actually closer to seven. Her fib is partly intentional (she doesn't want to appear a floozy), but mostly it's sexual amnesia. When a woman wants to pretend an encounter never occurred, she simply scratches the man from her official score sheet. Common excuses that lead to such an omission: The actual sex lasted only a few thrusts; or she was drunk or on the rebound.

5. I fantasized about being with you at least a dozen times before we actually first got naked.

6. I still think about my ex-boyfriends and compare them with you. Mostly you win. Sometimes not.

7. I have Googled your exes.

8. When I'm falling in love with you, I completely lose my appetite.

9. My body really isn't naturally this hairless and smooth all over. But I will never allow you to see any indication whatsoever of all the shaving, tweezing, waxing, exfoliating, and moisturizing that gets it this way.

10. I only appear to have it all together. My true organization (or lack thereof) is revealed in my closet, my makeup bag, my desk files.

11. I have discovered your porn stash and your frequently visited porn Web sites and think the things that turn you on are hilarious.

12. When I say, "I'm ready," I'll need exactly 7 more minutes to get ready. Don't try to cheat the system by showing up 7 minutes later; I will still need an extra 7 minutes.

13. When I say, "I'll meet you in 15 minutes," I mean I will leave in 15 minutes, and thus won't actually arrive for at least 30 (but probably more like 40).

14. You've made me cry more times than you'll ever know.

15. I obsess about when you're going to call me again. The period of time between our first date and your "Thanks for a

great night; when can I see you again?" always seems
stretched into slow motion. So don't worry about looking too
eager. Call. Even if you only wait until noon the day after, it
will feel like a lifetime to me. And don't send me an e-mail
unless you want me to put you in the figurative trash can
along with your message.

16. I want you to talk a little dirty.

17. At the beginning of our relationship, I save all of your voice mails
and listen to them (and make my friends listen, too), repeatedly.

18. I might wear granny underwear and purposely not shave my legs
because I like you. As crazy as it sounds, the more I like you, the less
likely I am to sleep with you on an early date because I don't want
to sabotage having a "proper" relationship with you. So I just might
purposely hunt out the ugliest underwear in my drawer and not
shave my legs—all to prevent myself from getting naked with you
too soon. Sometimes I might get a little tipsy or carried away and
this plan will backfire.

19. I split the cost of my fashion purchases over two or more credit
cards so you don't notice the gargantuan deficit.

**20. I'm constantly testing you. I observe, analyze, and judge
every action, word, gesture, e-mail, and facial expression.
When I ask you if you want to have a threesome, I don't mean
it. If you want me to speak to you again, let alone sleep with
you after this conversation, the answer should always be "Why
would I want to sleep with another woman when I have you?"**

21. I check out your butt every time you leave the room.

22. I need constant indications that you want me around. That's
why it's better, for example, to say, "I want you to come away with

me for the weekend. Could you come with me?" than to ask, "What are you up to this weekend?"

23. I love it when you get a little jealous. So if you ever see me flirting in front of you with the waiter, the bus driver, or another guy at a party, know I'm actually flirting with you—through him.

24. Even though I may complain that I don't see you enough (or that you work too hard), I find nothing sexier than watching you put on a suit in the morning and rush off to work.

25. I start fights with you because I'm feeling ignored. I'm trying to force emotion out of you. Don't retreat into your cave; just give me what I want: some attention. And never tell me to "calm down," unless you want to guarantee that I absolutely won't.

26. Even if I insist on paying or splitting the bill on our first date, I'll think you're cheap if you let me.

27. I may find your best friend repulsive, but I've fantasized about sleeping with him. Not because I want him but because I want a piece of a guy who is so close to you.

28. If I'm going to break up with you, all of my friends know way before you do. I've been talking about it for 2 weeks.

29. When we do break up, I put all photographs of you and mementos of our relationship in a shoe box and store it in my closet. Just in case I get nostalgic. Just in case you come back.

30. I want you to take control in bed. Yes, I have a successful career, I'm financially independent, I live on my own, and I don't need a man to make me happy (in theory). I still want you to pick me up, carry me to the bedroom, and take without asking.

MUST READS

First Time's the Charm

Forget beginner's luck. From "How do?" to "I do," 10 tips
to help you ace every critical relationship milestone

BY RON GERACI

ARCHED EYEBROW AT ONE O'CLOCK. Slightest hint of a smile. Could be random. But there's just enough eye contact to tell you it isn't. Her girlfriend is in the restroom . . . will be back at any moment. Seconds are ticking by. You could be wrong. But if life and Eminem lyrics have taught you anything at all, it's that you only get one shot.

Did you take it?

The first step to meeting a woman is up to you. For every important step thereafter, we've got your back. A little guidance from us, and you'll gracefully tackle every relationship challenge—the first time.

FIRST HELLO

If your deodorant is working, you have about 15 seconds to prove that you're not just another jackass who wants to get in her pants. You need to show confidence, nonthreatening charm, and a smidgen of aggressiveness to let her know you're decisive. If she looks at you for three beats, you're cleared for approach. Say something short and firm, like "Hi, great bracelet," suggests David Copeland, coauthor of *How to Talk to Women*. And follow it with a question—"What's the story behind that?"—suggests Copeland, to start her talking. After a few minutes of good conversation, ask for her phone number.

FIRST PHONE CALL

Only a fraction of the Mikes and Toms who ask for her number ever actually call her—a conundrum she regards as the Bermuda Triangle of male mysteries. She knows you're not calling for investment tips, so keep it quick and simple. Within 2 days, dial the number she gave you, identify yourself, and suggest a definite date. Say, "On Tuesday, would you like to go to dinner at Jack's Sturgeon House? I can pick you up at 8 o'clock." Always make the first date on a weekday night— weekend nights are strictly for third dates and onward. And never say, "If you happen to be free in the next week . . . "

FIRST DATE

She's here, so she's at least mildly interested in having sex with you. Or not totally repulsed. Same thing! The first date needs to broadcast a broad point, says Lou Paget, a sex educator in Los Angeles and the author of *365 Days of Sensational Sex*: You're not looking to get her naked before she's comfortable, but you are interested in getting naked with her. Keep the damage under $100; killing a wad would make her uneasy. Throughout the night, touch her protectively—like lightly resting your hand on her back as you guide her to the restaurant table. "It connotes that you're in charge of seeing that her body is safe," says Pat Allen, Ph.D., a relationship therapist in Los Angeles. To sow anticipation, end the date sooner than you'd like, with the unmistakable gesture of a mature man who's interested: Place your hand on her hip and give her a decisive on-the-lips kiss. Call her within 24 hours to tell her you had a good time and to ask her out again.

FIRST-TIME SEX

Taking off your clothes with a new woman is always uncharted territory. The key to great sex the first time is taking it slow. "Let her know that when you make love to a woman, you do it from head to toe," says Nicole Beland, *Men's Health*'s Girl Next Door. "Few guys know how much a woman loves to be stroked with her bra and panties still on,

so don't rush to get her naked. Show her you understand the importance of foreplay by slowly rubbing circles over her clitoris and nipples. The feel of the fabric against her skin and your fingers on the
other side of it will leave her dying for more."

At T minus 30 seconds, retrieve a three-pack of Trojans (a whole
box is scary) from your bedside table and tell her you're going to use
one—saying it aloud increases trust, according to a University of
Georgia study. After sex, hold her for at least 10 minutes, says Ava
Cadell, Ph.D., Ed.D., a sex therapist and the author of *12 Steps to
Everlasting Love*, "tell her she has a great body (and mean it), and stay
the night." This shows reverence for her body and reassures her that
you want sex to be part of the journey of the relationship, not the destination.

FIRST MORNING AFTER

There are three rules after you've spent the night: Stay, snuggle, and
enjoy yourself (pretend, if you have to). If you must leave to tend to
your philanthropies, make the journey a joint offer. Even if it's
5:08 A.M., a nicely whispered "Shall we get some breakfast?" will let
her roll over without thinking you're a fleeing bastard.

FIRST TIME MEETING HER PARENTS

This doesn't have to be the slice of hell it sometimes becomes. "It's
very significant to gain the approval of her parents," says Sol Gordon,
Ph.D., a professor emeritus of child and family studies at Syracuse
University. If Arthur and Madge suspect you're putting on an act to
end up on their good side, they'll assume you're slimy. That's bad.
Nearly one in seven women reports telling a lover to scram because
her parents didn't like the guy.

To calm their worst fears, bring them a small gift, like a plant, or
a bottle of wine or dessert to go with dinner. It's old-fashioned, and
old-fashioned men are less likely to run white slavery rings. Ask rapid-

fire questions ("Are those imported Hummels?") to start them talking. The less you actually say, though, the smarter you'll sound. Whenever the conversation lags, bring up their daughter's magnificent accomplishments—like the promotion she got at work or the 5-K she recently ran. After your visit, send her parents a thank-you note—the extra touch that will impress them.

FIRST SERIOUS RELATIONSHIP TALK

When she inevitably asks, "Where is this relationship going?" don't ask her to define her views first (as a lot of guys do); anything you say after that will seem like a response calculated to fit hers. Instead, gently take her hand and say, "I've been thinking about that, too," advises Aline Zoldbrod, Ph.D., a psychologist and relationship expert in Lexington, Massachusetts. List about five specific things you like about her (her laugh, her smell, her map-reading skills, and such). Then say you don't know precisely where things are going because, naturally, learning to know someone is a slow process. End your soliloquy with the Teflon coup de grâce that will always save your ass, and often has the added power of being true: "I do know one thing: This relationship has promise."

FIRST FIGHT

Things are going swimmingly, but at some point you will get in an argument. Bloodfest Number One is the pivotal test of whether you'll make it as a couple or not, says Gordon. She'll judge you on three revealing factors: How cruel you are, how much you listen, and how long you stay pissed. Be careful to hold back personal insults. "If one slips out, apologize right away," warns Gordon. Those grenades will stick in her brain forever. And if the argument drags on for more than 10 minutes, initiate sex with her as a distraction. Promise to listen to her vitriol tomorrow, and do so. This shows maturity. And in the morning, after the roses you ordered arrive, she'll already have forgiven you.

FIRST VACATION TOGETHER

A little planning goes a long way to ensure a pleasant first trip together. Develop a loose idea of the few key things you both absolutely want to do (beach naps, rappelling, macramé), and then, even more important, lay a blueprint for time apart. The rightish words: "I don't want to bore you with a lot of the dumb crap I'm going to do, so why don't we take a couple of hours each day and do our own thing?" This will save you from being dragged through a 9-mile purse bazaar, and her from enduring the Continental Tire Bowl.

FIRST "YES" THAT COSTS YOU SEVEN GRAND

The platinum rule for marriage proposals: Forget clichés like doing it at the top of the Empire State Building or using the Jumbotron at the stadium. She'll have to defend your originality forever, and you'll become more riddled with guilt with every episode of *The Bachelor* you catch. Instead, "put yourself in her shoes and figure out what she would find romantic and memorable," says Jason Rich, author of *Will You Marry Me: Popping the Question with Romance and Style*. For example, if she's the outdoorsy type, she might think a proposal while you're hiking together is romantic.

Plan in advance and even rehearse aloud what you want to say and the sentiment you want to convey, but not to the point where it's a verbatim script. "If you try to completely wing it, you might actually forget to ask her to marry you or forget to say, 'I love you,'" says Rich. To ring her coo bell before you give her a ring, produce an obscure memento that you've saved from early in your relationship, such as a love note or a concert ticket stub.

Grant Her Wishes

With a little thought, you can find her a gift
that inspires gratitude—and more

BY JENNIFER BENJAMIN

IT'S NO SECRET that you want a plasma TV—you visit it at Circuit City once a week, have its picture on the night table. And you talk about it. Women, in contrast, seldom just come out and ask for what they want. It's kind of a test. "She wants to know that the man in her life cares about her and thinks about her enough to come up with the perfect gift," says Paul Coleman, Psy.D., a psychologist and the author of *How to Say It for Couples*. "If he gets her what she wants, she thinks he must really get her." The good news is that she's dropping hints, and we can help you pick them up. Read on to learn how.

RADAR. Take mental notes (or real notes; they keep better) on the clothes she's wearing, the jewelry she likes, the bands she's listening to. "My tried-and-true trick is to make passing comments like 'None of my nighties look good anymore. I totally need new ones,'" says Sara, 28. "I'm so obvious about it, my husband would have to be clueless not to notice."

INTERROGATION. You'll need to ask questions. Not "So, whaddaya want this year?" Something like "You wear hoop earrings a lot. Are they your favorite?" Then listen. She'll either respond with "Yeah, I love them, but I want some new ones" or say, "I have way too many, but I really want a new necklace." Translation: She wants a necklace.

SPYING. Flip through her catalogs and see if she's marked anything. Or browse through a magazine together and note where she pauses. "While my boyfriend and I are sitting around, I'll open up to something I like and ask him if he thinks it's cute or tell him I've been looking for a dress just like it," says Jenny, 26. Is that obvious enough for you?

BACKUP. Call in reinforcements—her friends. They shop with her and know way more than you do about her sizes, tastes, and current wardrobe. Ask one of them for advice on what to get your woman. "I always tell my sister everything I want, and without fail, my husband goes to her for advice," says Monique, 29. Sure, there's the chance her network will report back, but at least she'll know you were making the effort.

Here are some thoughts from women we know. Let their inspired ideas inspire you. . . .

I pointed out a suede jacket that looked like one I'd lost on a trip. I didn't even think my husband heard me, but that's what I unwrapped on Christmas morning. —DESIREE, 32

My guy was low on funds one Valentine's Day. I'm a teacher, so instead of a present, he came as my date to my class party. You can't put a price tag on that. —ARIEL, 26

The best gift I ever got was an import CD that I couldn't track down. While I was recovering from surgery, my boyfriend brought it to me. That was beyond thoughtful. —SUE, 23

My boyfriend complimented my earrings, and I told him I'd had no luck finding a matching necklace. Months later, he gave me a necklace he'd had made. —HOLLY, 27

Instant Heat

33 easy ways to get a woman hot fast—and a few ideas
for what you can do once she is. Tip one: Read your favorites
aloud to each other

BY TED SPIKER AND SISKI GREEN

MOST BEDROOM PROBLEMS boil down to this: Men are microwaves and women are Crock-Pots.

With men, all you have to do is push a few buttons and we're hotter than a habanero. But with women, it's an all-day process. You have to buy all the ingredients, you have to mix them together, and then you have to put everything in the pot and let this mouthwatering dish simmer . . . and simmer . . . and simmer.

While some of us search for more sex and others of us search for better sex, almost all of us search for faster ways to get more and better sex. That's why we're offering a microwave mentality for the Crock-Pot reality: quick, easy things you can do to make her heating speeds better match yours. All of our suggestions—from the romance to the climax—will take you anywhere from a few seconds to a few minutes. The payoff? They'll instantly ratchet up her knobs to high heat.

ROMANCE

BUY HER A SILK THONG. A gift of lingerie is cliché, right? So twist it. Give it to her when you (seemingly) don't expect sex right then and there. Pass it to her under the table at a restaurant, and ask her go to the ladies' room and change into it. "It's a little bit naughty, but she has a chance to play back," says Joy Davidson, Ph.D., a relationship and sex therapist in Seattle. Not recommended for a first date.

EMBRACE HER UNTIL SHE MAKES THE MOVE TO LEAVE. Good kissing tops most women's list of turn-ons. But nothing takes the place of good hugging, especially if you let her initiate it. "Let her know how much you want her to hug you, how much you savor it," says Lou Paget, author of *365 Days of Sensational Sex*. Make it clear you don't want the hug to end.

WEAR HER NAME. Women love to hear men use their names. The more unexpected the place—like in the middle of a sentence—the better. Better still, write her name on your shoulder, your hand, or anyplace she'll have a chance of spotting it. It's a tattoo without pain—one that gives only pleasure. "It will make her laugh and think you're so adorable," says Davidson. "But what it says to her is 'You matter.'"

WHISPER INTO HER EAR. In public, at a party, tell her what you want to do to her later: "Tonight I'm going to make you have as many orgasms as is physically possible." For women, thinking of what might happen later can be just as exciting as what actually happens.

SKIP THE FLOWERS. Blooms at the office are standard protocol. If you want to stand out, send a card instead. "It's really the thoughtful things you do in nonsexual times that make a woman want you," says Paul Joannides, author of *Guide to Getting It On!* Go with a thank-you. Write out a few things you've never thanked her for—for making breakfast on Sunday, for cleaning your stubble out of the sink. An appreciated woman during the day is an appreciative woman at night.

PLANT A PICTURE. Stash a photo of her in your wallet. She'll deny it, but all women rummage at some point. Turn it to your advantage.

SAY WHY. Anyone can say, "I love you," so explain why. Maybe it's the way she nibbles at a Kit Kat, or how her nose scrunches when she drinks tequila. The more unique your reasons, the more special she'll feel.

GET YOUR STORY STRAIGHT. For a happy ending, remember the beginning: the details of your first meeting—where you were, what she was wearing, what you said, and how you felt. Recount them. Often.

MAKE YOURSELF SICK. Leave love notes around the house—in the fridge, on the bathroom mirror, under her pillow. That much sweetness might make you nauseated, but it'll make her feel like a lovesick teenager.

PUT HER LIPSTICK ON HER. "Grooming a woman is kind of a role reversal," says Linda De Villers, Ph.D., a California sex therapist and the author of *Love Skills: A Fun, Upbeat Guide to Sex-cessful Relationships*. "She's being doted on and served, and it shows that you think a certain part of her body is attractive." Other ideas: shave her legs, paint her toenails, or brush or wash her hair. According to a menshealth.com poll of 3,200 men, 76 percent said they have shampooed their woman's hair. And *Men's Health* readers don't waste their time on things that don't work.

FOREPLAY

KISS AND LICK HER HINGES. You've got the obvious kiss spots covered. Now concentrate your efforts elsewhere—on her elbows, knees,

7 Hot Things to Say to a Woman

"I love your eyelashes."

"Sex with you just gets better and better."

"You look beautiful when you're sleeping."

"The way you dance is really sexy."

"You have a wonderful laugh."

"You're so clever."

"Your skin smells fantastic."

shoulders, ankles, neck, and hip joints. "They're rarely attended to with long caresses," says Davidson. "It's a super sensation." See if you can make her come unhinged.

BEAR FRUIT. Chocolate syrup and whipped cream get all the kinky play in movies. Instead, turn her body into a juicer. "The best foods for sex are fruits that you can rub onto the body, such as soft mango or papaya," says Ava Cadell, Ph.D., Ed.D., a sex therapist in California and the author of *12 Steps to Everlasting Love.* "Then bury your face and devour both her and the fruit." Get sticky, shower, repeat. If you're Mickey Rourke, skip the shower.

AND BERRIES. Forget coffee and toast—bring hot chocolate (a sexual stimulant for her) and raspberries and strawberries to bed. The berries replenish the zinc you lose when you ejaculate—5 milligrams, or a third of your daily requirement. Okay, it's not Viagra-on-a-vine, but murmuring a fact like that makes you seem like you know everything about sex. Which can be sexy.

TRY THE NO-MOVE MOVE. When you start foreplay, tell her you're not going to move on to another action until she tells you what to do next. This works physically and mentally: It's a way to encourage her to open up and direct you to what she really wants. Now your turn.

GIVE HER A MASSAGE. But make it interesting:

• Roll a chilled can of soda along the backs of her thighs (in hot weather).
• Warm a towel in the microwave for 10 seconds and massage her with that (in cool weather).
• Shake salt onto her belly and lick it off. Add tequila as desired.
• Turn winter gloves inside out, put them on, and massage her with the soft side.

GIVE HER CHILLS. "Cold is sensed by more nerve endings than mere touch can reach, so you're expanding her range of response," says Phillip Hodson, a British sex therapist. Do this: Chill a bunch of grapes for at least 20 minutes. Then trail a small sprig of them along her neck, nipples, and inner thighs. Nibble away. Now take a grape and put it in your mouth, gently pressing it up against her clitoris by puckering up your lips. (Hold it in your teeth if necessary.)

COME CLEAN. Here's a master class in the notoriously tricky art of bath sex. Start by slinging in a generous quantity of bath gel, advises Anne Hooper, a sex therapist and the author of *Ultimate Sex Guide*. Fill the tub with 5 inches of hot water; then pour more foaming bath gel onto your bellies, chests, and legs. Then have her lie on top of you and use her body as a scrubbing brush. Throw in Rub-a-Dub Dice ($10), floating foam cubes with sexy commands, or Rubba Ducky ($35), a vibrating version of the classic, both available at mypleasure.com.

RUB HER DOWN. For extra shower power, pour a couple of drops of shower gel into a spritz bottle and mix it with water. Spray her; then rub. She'll feel three different types of stimulation—the steady pelting of the shower, the soft spray of the soapy gel, and the firm caresses of your hands. That's the kind of threesome that turns *her* on.

SEX

MAKE A BEDROOM BURRITO. Bondage is appealing for a good reason: It heightens the anticipation for the one who's receiving the pleasure. But anything with locks, Velcro, or ties can freak her out (us, too), so try this: While you're rolling around in bed, roll her up in the sheet so she can't do anything with her arms (think burrito or straitjacket). Leave her head, shoulders, and lower legs exposed. Now kiss, lick, and caress every exposed inch of skin. It's simple, spontaneous, and soft-core.

BLINDFOLD YOURSELF. Many women who are insecure about their bodies stick to the missionary position because you can't see them. If you really can't see her because your eyes are covered, she'll do a lot more with you, to you, and for you.

Women Confess: The Sexiest Thing a Man Can Do in Bed

Steal these ideas that worked for other guys.

Make her wait. "I finally got into bed with this amazing guy who I assumed would devour me whole. Instead, he took off my clothes, sat on me, and spent about 45 minutes tracing the outlines of my body with his fingertips without saying a single word. By the end I was hypnotized with pleasure—then he left! This made him not only totally sexy but totally sensual, which is much harder to achieve."—ANDREA, 27, EDITOR, NEW YORK CITY

Make her pucker up. "I had this boyfriend who would hover above me, gently gliding his lips over mine, but pulling back the second I'd lift my head up to reach his. He'd do this over and over, almost kissing me but not quite. It was so erotic, and the lead-up made the real kissing much more powerful."—ELIZABETH, 30, ATTORNEY, WASHINGTON, DC

Make her feel sexy. "I'm not exactly what one would call petite, and I was dating a guy who was very wiry and thin. We were hooking up, and I was a self-conscious because my more-than-tiny rear was quite visible. He whispered in my ear, 'You know, you have the sweetest ass.' I still reflect on his voice in my ear. And by the way, he was

JUST BEFORE YOU ENTER HER, ASK PERMISSION. "Some women find it incredibly endearing," says Barnaby Barratt, Ph.D., president of the American Association of Sex Educators, Counselors, and Therapists. "It gives them a sense of respect. It gives them the security to become more sexually relaxed." And when you're first entering her, kiss her lips or caress her face. "Give her some kind of stimulation in addition to penetration," De Villers says.

PRACTICE REENTRY. After you first enter her, do it again—slowly. Repeat it over and over. "One of the huge turn-ons is anticipation," well-rewarded for this admission."—RACHEL, 34, MARKETING FIRM OWNER, BROOKLYN, NY

Make her sticky. "I came home from work one night to find my boyfriend in our bedroom, which was lit solely by candles. He'd gotten a plastic tarp, one of those things that painters put down, and spread it over the bed and onto the floor. And he'd covered it with massage and baby oil. I was shocked but intrigued at the same time, and couldn't believe that he took the initiative. Armed with that much oil, you're able to do things that you never imagined. Trust me."—KAREN, 34, SALES EXECUTIVE, LOS ANGELES

Make her melt. "After the first time we slept together, my man came back to bed with a plate loaded with four ice cream sandwiches, two caramel ice cream bars, a bowl of French vanilla ice cream, a pile of chocolate chip cookies, and a glass of milk. Our clothes were scattered all over the room, we were still a little sweaty, and we sat naked in the center of his big white bed, licking cookie crumbs from our fingertips. It was decadent and sexy and unforgettable."—CECILIA, 24, STUDENT, AUSTIN, TEXAS

—REPORTING BY ALLISON WINN SCOTCH

De Villers says. "Don't pull out all the way, but when you pull almost all the way out, she gets the anticipation of the stroke that comes back in."

DO IT IN PUBLIC. Or just pretend. Exhibitionism is a secret thrill for many women, but the threat of arrest deters them. So have sex standing up, with her near the bedroom window. It's easy to duck out of the way. If she's semiclothed, your neighbors will be none the wiser.

BLOW BUBBLES. Take a swig of champagne before going down, keep it in your mouth by creating a "seal" with your lips, and then use your tongue to swirl the bubbles around the head of her clitoris. Nerve endings react to bubbles. In a good way.

USE THE COTTONS CYCLE. "The washing machine is the biggest vibrator in the house," says Hodson. Sit on it and have her sit on top of you—the vibrations carry through your penis. Cottons get the longest, fastest spin.

GO INTO THE CLOSET. Novelty is an aphrodisiac. Any unusual setting, with strange sensations, smells, and muffled sounds, will make sex feel new—or it'll make you nostalgic for the days of sneaking some

The Hottest Man I Know: The Nice-Guy Badass

Like most women I know, I have a Tobey Maguire–Keith Richards complex. In a nutshell, it's this: Good guys are boring and bad boys aren't worth the trouble. These days, the man who ranks sexiest in my mind is the one who falls somewhere in the middle. That's why my boyfriend, John, is hotter than any other guy I've ever met.

Back when John was just my guitar teacher, he kept his strong opinions and sexual energy under wraps. All I saw was his patient, nurturing side. He absorbed my nervousness and embarrassment like a sponge, and gave back gentle encouragement and soft-spoken instructions. He was obviously hot and talented, but his Tobey-like demeanor had me convinced that he was a shy loner. Not ideal, but enough to make me call him one day last August and ask him out for a beer.

Over six or seven dates, I discovered that this quiet, unassuming musician was harboring a lot of Keith. He'd dated exceptionally gorgeous, interesting women and had a cast of engaging friends, including a midget drummer and a guy named Scum who lived in his laundry room for a few months in the late 1990s. He had performed regularly at some of New York City's most legendary rock clubs with legs spread wide and pelvis thrust forward. In addition to being a sweetheart, it turned out, Johnny was, and still is, a badass.

in wherever you could hide. Confined spaces add urgency because you won't linger. "They're great for a quickie," says sex therapist Louanne Cole Weston. Watch that shoe tree!

WORK THE ANGLE. Liberator Shapes (liberator.com) velvet cushions create an "orgasm optimum" 26-degree pelvic tilt, which means maximum contact between your body and her clitoris, and minimum demands for foreplay. Feel free to adjust the angle *slightly*—there's some evidence that 27 degrees works as well.

OR CALL A SQUEEZE PLAY. With her facedown and you on top, get

What makes this duality so sexy is it allows him to play all the roles of an ideal boyfriend. He understands the line between spontaneity and unreliability, playfulness and childishness. He'll praise the finer points of *Grand Theft Auto III* and a Bill Evans jazz piano solo in a single breath. Man, that turns me on. He can also work knots out of my long hair, build a computer from spare parts, make a delicious marinara sauce from scratch, tell me to go to hell when I'm being unreasonable, and talk about his or my emotions without acting like he's doing me a favor.

But the sexiest thing about John, which could eventually hook me for life: He doesn't spread himself too thin, do things halfway, or reveal his private self to just anyone. When he does decide to devote himself to a project or open himself up to someone, it's with high intensity and rare loyalty. One morning I watched him decorate a birthday cake for his 4-year-old niece. As he began to frost a #1 on Thomas the Tank Engine, I could tell that the rest of the world had faded away. When he's focused on me, I feel like I'm getting 500 percent of his attention. He doesn't play games about how much time he wants to spend together, and he doesn't hold back when he feels like grabbing me and carrying me to bed. His passion is directed carefully but expressed with total abandon—it's so damn sexy I can't imagine ever getting enough.   —Nicole Beland, *Men's Health* Girl Next Door her to cross her legs—positioning yours outside of hers. Her vagina will feel tighter, and the added friction means more pleasure.

ROCK HER WORLD. Hook up on a rocking or swivel chair. The unpredictable rocking motion adds a fourth dimension to the experience, says Cole Weston. Why do you think Granny is always smiling?

GET BIGGER. When you're on top, place her legs over your shoulders. This shortens her vaginal canal, making your penis feel bigger inside her. Plus, you're guaranteed more sensation.

STAND BY YOUR WOMAN. For better from-behind sex, have her kneel on the edge of the bed with her upper chest touching the mattress. This creates a steep angle for her back and elongates the vaginal barrel—making it feel tighter. You get a fantastic view, and she'll

The Hottest Man I Know: The Cusack Cliché

Back when my mom came of age, big-screen sex symbols were of a certain solitary, brooding variety. James Garner, Steve McQueen, Paul Newman. They were bruisers—mystery men who slung their virility around like a six-shooter. I never went for the type. Too hairy.

Instead, my movie ideal is of another genre entirely—a 1980s romantic comedy to their 1960s Western. Like millions of women my age (let's say 29), no movie hero sends my heart thumping like John Cusack's character Lloyd Dobler in *Say Anything*.

I know what you're thinking: What a tool. And granted, a guy shows up outside my window at 1 A.M. blaring Peter Gabriel and I'm calling the cops. But I love a man who knows what he wants, especially if it happens to be me. Call me selfish, but I want to be assured of my importance, my irreplaceability in someone's heart. As a college student, I fell head over platform shoes for a chef who devoted an entire weekend to wooing me by cooking elaborate meals in an apartment we never left. I was impressed by his skills (in the kitchen!), but I was enjoy having her nipples stimulated by rubbing on the mattress. Everyone wins.

MAKE IT EASY. For oral sex, stand while your partner kneels or sits on the bed. This angle lets her take more of you, gives her better control, and is less tiring (so she can keep going).

LET HER GIVE YOU A PEARL NECKLACE. But not a real one. Give her a fake pearl necklace and ask her to use it on you. Paget gives the details: Lightly lubricate the pearls and your penis. Then have your partner wrap the pearls around the shaft and slowly stroke up and down with a gentle rotation. The beads provide a smooth texture that gets warm when in contact with your skin, creating a totally new level of sensation.

knocked out by his determination—he wanted me, and it was intoxicating. I've heard from guys who swear such behavior backfires—women think it's too much, too creepy. In some cases, that's true. All I know is that the chef went after what he wanted, and he got it.

Back to Lloyd. He's not so handsome, really, and this is a key point: Charisma counts. His attractiveness comes from his quick wit, his generous smile. I can't tell you how often a girlfriend has described the object of her affection thusly: "He's not that good-looking, but there's just something about him." A swagger, an aura. My first boyfriend was the color of wood pulp and could practically fit in my pocket, but he had charisma to burn. He was hilarious and kind, and when he spoke, people leaned in to hear what he said. Because he wasn't conventionally handsome, I always figured I was alone in my attraction, and it alternately frustrated and delighted me, like an amazing indie band only I knew. When we broke up, though, women stampeded for his number.   —Sarah Hepola

Don't Get Roped In

How to slip a woman's knottiest questions

BY SARAH MILLER

W E WOMEN ENJOY TALKING—and after a lifetime of dating, you should have the flattened cilia in your ears to prove it. But blithe banter over martinis and cashews doesn't last forever. Once things turn serious, you're going to have serious conversations.

The good news: You don't have to get pulled into drawn-out discourse or end up arguing or revisiting the same exchange you thought you'd sorted out last week. Mastery is within your reach. Here, the top six questions every woman is hardwired to ask, and when she's likely to ask them.

1. "Where is this relationship going?"

BE ON THE LOOKOUT: After you've had sex but before you've agreed not to see other people.

WHY IS THIS HAPPENING TO ME? Because the Man Who Is Really Interested and the Man Who Is Really Not Interested have a strange ability to behave identically. We need to know: Do you have the potential to fall in love with us?

THE RESPONSES:

IF THIS IS GOING SOMEWHERE: A slight prevarication—"I'm glad we're talking about this because I want you to know I am really interested in you"—should work. She needs to hear that you like her specifically, not just that you like having a little company when you're eating and having orgasms.

IF THIS IS GOING NOWHERE: Quickly introduce that small part of her who hopes your apathy is actually masking depths of passion to the larger part of her who knows that is bullsh---.

2. "Tell me about your ex-girlfriends."

BE ON THE LOOKOUT: When she begins relating lengthy anecdotes about her exes. She's trying to create an atmosphere of mutual sharing, which you, my sadly pussy-whipped friend, are about to fall for.

WHY IS THIS HAPPENING TO ME? Because your girlfriend is obsessed. Not with your exes, or even with you, but with herself. She's not interested in your past relationships per se; she's interested in what they say about her.

THE RESPONSE: Emphasize that your sizable, but not overly indulgent, love and erotic experience has been in the company of beautiful, talented, smart women. She'll do the logic: He's dated women who were beautiful, talented, and smart. Therefore, I am beautiful and talented and smart! When discussing "how things ended" in the past, present yourself as the man who has never found the right woman to love and understand him, but also the man who has never found a woman quite worthy of his best behavior. It's all spin.

3. "Tell me about your family."

BE ON THE LOOKOUT: When you've been together long enough—3 months—that she expects a steady stream of emotional sharing. You know: Ideas. Feelings.

WHY IS THIS HAPPENING TO ME? She'd like to find you fascinating, maybe even deep; but she needs a good backstory to confirm this.

THE RESPONSE: Start with some family photos. Then, at family gatherings, share sensitive "observations" with her to show that you're emotionally in touch with your family: "My father seems a little lost now that he's retired."

4. "Should we move in together?"

BE ON THE LOOKOUT: If she's been saying things like "God, I am so sick of walking around with my underwear in my bag."

WHY IS THIS HAPPENING TO ME? In an ideal world, after too many nights of "My place or yours?" both of you would blurt out at the very same time, "Let's live together!" This not being an ideal world, and women being more inclined to demand momentum, it's often her suggestion.

THE RESPONSES: If you've been thinking the same thing, call the movers, and good luck to you. If not, tell her everything you imagine you'd enjoy about living together: waking up to her, seeing her even if you didn't have specific plans. This creates a favorable environment for expressing your reservations, about which you should be specific. Tell her you've always lived with roommates, and you want some time to live alone. Bring up pursuits—writing, meditation, compulsive masturbation (maybe not)—that require a degree of independence, but make sure you're already involved in them. "I can't live with you because I have to start my screenplay" is weak.

5. "Do you think of this as a long-term relationship?"

(May also be stated as "Are we getting married or what, you giant a---hole?")

BE ON THE LOOKOUT: If (a) you're dating a girl who is definitely the marrying kind, (b) more than 2 years have passed, or (c) she's over 30.

WHY IS THIS HAPPENING TO ME? Because your girlfriend is annoyed at herself for having potentially wasted years of her life.

THE RESPONSE: She wants to know when she's getting her damn engagement ring and, in the absence of a satisfactory answer, when you're coming to get your stuff. Spare her your feelings on this one. If the answer isn't weighed in carats, she's not interested.

6. "Why don't we talk anymore?"

BE ON THE LOOKOUT: If there are extended, unexplained silences on her part. It may be her passive-aggressive way of saying, "I'm sick of filling these conversational holes."

WHY IS THIS HAPPENING TO ME? If you don't erupt hourly with an Old Faithful-like gusher of steaming words and opinions, she'll imagine that the hot, subterranean stratum of your relationship has cooled.

THE RESPONSE: You will be tempted to refer to your stellar contribution to all the conversations above. You will think about saying, "What do you want to talk about?" Don't. Applying male logic to female emotion is about as smart as throwing gas on a fire. "We don't talk anymore" is unsubtle code for "I'm starting to think you're a bore, and I wish you'd change my mind." So start. Ask more questions. Give longer answers. Read a book and tell her about it. You're undoubtedly fascinating, but you have to market yourself, every day, to ensure she keeps buying.

Anatomy of an Affair

New sex. Illicit sex. Dangerous sex.
Can you resist? Should you?

BY LAURENCE ROY STAINS

SOONER OR LATER, every married man meets Kristi. You know Kristi. She's right over there in the next cubicle. She's your neighbor. Or your best friend's sister.

God, she's just . . . great, you say to yourself. So friendly, so cute, so upbeat. You're thinking about her. Okay, you've started to fantasize. Just a little. And you suspect she's fantasizing about you because when you saw her yesterday, there was that . . . moment. Not to sound corny, but it was a moment of reckoning. She looked into your eyes and didn't look away. Finally, it's started to dawn on you: You've got something she wants.

And you're tempted to give it to her.

All right, deep breath: You didn't embark on the journey of marriage with the idea that you'd get to take a few detours, and you certainly didn't think you'd turn into one of "those guys." But then, most men don't. They have stumbled accidentally onto their own little Temptation Island. There they are, standing helplessly in its spell and face-to-face with what the nuns in parochial school used to call "an occasion of sin." But what do nuns know about love? This can't be sin; it doesn't feel the least bit sinful. She's a sweet, smiling, loving person; in a way, your friendly banter reminds you of the kind of talks you used to have with your wife—before all that baggage got in the way. And you think to yourself, Why does everybody else get to have all the fun? Why can't I join the club?

You can. You da man! And I'm going to lay it all out for you, step-by-step. Your fling with Kristi will pass through four stages.

STAGE 1: ATTRACTION

I'm guessing you work with Kristi. Most affairs begin at the office. Work is where you are a master, where you shine, where you are plugged into all your power sources. You do what you do with skill, confidence, and humor. Women want that in a guy. Toss into that mix a wardrobe of suits, ties, short skirts, and high heels, and it's no wonder so many romances blossom in the workplace. And lately Kristi seems to be in no hurry to go home at night.

Time to bump it up a notch.

It all starts so innocently. You trade notes and silly e-mails. You both show up at the same after-work gatherings. You grab a bite for lunch. But when you start meeting for drinks, you're both hunting for something. She orders a sex on the beach and makes a little joke. My friend, your plane is number one for takeoff. A hungry itch comes over you, and you will not be denied.

STAGE 2: ECSTASY

You haven't felt like this since high school. Actually, you never felt like this in high school because the girls were more interested in the jocks and the heads. But it does feel like you're in love for the very first time. You're on cloud nine. The drink-after-work thing has turned into bottles of Dom Perignon. Kisses have become *Kama Sutra* positions. At the No-Tell Motel, the two of you engage in idle postcoital pillow talk about going somewhere beautiful together, like Paris. You can't even pronounce "croissant," but you're dreaming of Paris.

The rest of your life is on autopilot. Your boss is dropping dark hints about how "distracted" you seem lately. Big deal. You're in love. Nothing and no one can stand between you!

Well, except for your wife and kids. But let's not get ahead of our story.

Is the sex better? Of course it's better. It's new. Nothing beats new sex—the exploration of her every inch, the discovery and mapping and conquest of her sweet spots. Nothing is better than the praise she lavishes. Nothing makes you hotter than seeing her so aroused.

And this is not just new sex, my friend; this is illicit sex—which is way steamier. The added elements of secrecy and danger are time-honored ways to heighten arousal. (Every member of the Mile-High Club can tell you that.)

The secrecy is so much fun that most couples having affairs ignore the obvious: Everyone knows. *Everyone.* It's such fine sport to watch lovers deluding themselves with the belief that they're being perfectly discreet. Meanwhile, they glow like those radioactive monsters in Japanese sci-fi flicks of the 1950s. Frankly, you're starting to draw a crowd.

STAGE 3: COMPLICATION

One Monday morning, you get the e-mail you've been dreading.

"We *must* talk. Lunch?"

Kristi pours out a long, sad story of a hellish weekend. She says Steve suspects. He was in a rage. It's only because of heavy makeup that you can't see how hard he slapped her. You're thinking, That's not something makeup can cover. She's saying she needs to get out of her marriage. You'll help her, won't you, honey? She looked at an apartment early this morning before work, and it's great—right near here!—but they want 2 months' rent up front. If you could put down the two grand . . .

You got your American Express bill on Saturday. It's for $3,614.28. You don't have $3,614.28. You don't have two grand. And you thought love was free.

You fall silent. Now she's looking at you. She wasn't ready for this silence. You weren't ready for this moment.

That's one sob story; there are a million others. They all have the same plot development: You're about to be discovered. And the offended parties in these instances rarely take the news lying down. Usually they suffer as loudly as they can.

You're pressured to break up with her. She's wondering whether to break up with you—or him. Are you ready for that? No, you're not ready for that. You realize, a little late, that you're not ready for any of that.

STAGE 4: REMORSE AND MAYHEM

This stage is summarized in a single question: How the hell did I get myself into this?

Sometimes the only thing worse than getting caught is *not* getting caught. The good news is, you get away with it. And the bad news is, you get away with it. Kristi is really starting to annoy you, but you're too weak to give up the extra sex. You turn passive, and in response she becomes persistent. You're wondering how to get rid of her. She's wondering when you're going to leave your wife for her, the way you sort of hinted you would . . . didn't you?

She knows where you work, where you live. She knows where your wife works. Your dilemma is clear: To extricate yourself from this relationship, you're going to have to break the heart of the one person who can destroy you with a phone call.

That's if it ever gets to that stage. More likely, you'll be caught. In which case, one of two things will happen. You'll get divorced or stay married. If you get divorced, prepare to be broke and lonely. If you stay married, let me ask you something: Do you think your marriage will ever be the same? And if she does stick it out with you, despite the advice of all her friends and family, is it for a good reason, like she really, really loves you? Or is it for a convenient reason, like you make a nice salary?

In any case, patching up the marriage will require major-league groveling on your part. In return, you can expect zero trust, zero slack, and quite possibly a "retaliatory" affair on her part. As for your reputation and good standing with friends, family, and community, well, there will be blood on the floor.

Lucky you if the bleeding is metaphorical. Sometimes, someone goes into a cold, jealous rage. Someone's pride can't handle the idea that his wife cheated on him. Someone can't face the practical consequences of a wrecked marriage—selling the house, making child-support payments, facing the nosiness or sympathy of virtual strangers.

Oops. I'm so sorry.

You, too. You were expecting a happy ending. A *happy* ending! You are so funny. This story has been told a million times, in a million ways, for a million years. Never is there a happy ending. But you knew that. Didn't you?

Why Women Cheat

More and more women are unfaithful to their husbands.
Has the No-Tell Motel become the latest front line
in the battle of the sexes?

BY ELISSA SCHAPPELL

T HE BOYS ARE, AS USUAL, fighting in the back of the minivan. Their 3-year-old sister is wedged in a car seat between them, crying. Denise (name changed) tries to remember whether she put "Have a great day" notes in their lunch bags. She makes a note to buy ground chuck at the store later. Tonight is meat loaf night, as her husband, Paul, reminded her as he kissed her forehead on his way out the door. At school, she hops out of the car, kisses her boys on the forehead at the curb, and zips up their coats. They wave at her and tromp up the school steps.

Denise checks her watch. Next stop, the day care center. Thankfully, today there are no tears, clinging, or whimpering, which always make her feel guilty for putting her little girl in day care until 3 o'clock. She suspects the caregivers don't approve of her leaving her child so she can run errands, but what choice does she have? She has to go to the hardware store, pick up Paul's shirts, pay the mortgage, drop bags of clothes off at their church for the annual coat drive, return calls about after-school playdates, schedule the parent-teacher conferences, and, most important, sign the boys up for soccer.

She sits at the light. She can see the hardware store, but when the light goes green, she turns left instead of right. It is as if she's on autopilot. In 20 minutes, she is parking on a side street in a slightly run-down neighborhood far away from the large 1980s-style homes that make up her own. She wants to sit for a minute and listen to the end of Cheap Trick's "Surrender," but she doesn't dare. She pulls her ponytail loose and shakes her hair into her face. For a moment, crossing the street, she feels glamorous and mysterious. On the doorstep of a familiar house, she rings the bell, forcing herself not to look over her shoulder to see if she is being watched.

Although Tom is rubbing sleep out of his eyes—he has been working long hours since he started his own landscaping business—he is surprised and happy to see her. "Baby," he says, "don't you look good," and pulls her in. He is shorter than her husband, but much more muscular. She'd met him at the gym after the birth of her first child.

He undresses her as she steps inside, removing her clothes like she is a present he can't wait to unwrap, and then he f---s her on the floor. She likes the way he insists on making love with the lights on, and the way he sometimes holds her arms behind her back when he kisses her. She likes it when he goes down on her—something Paul stopped doing after their first year of marriage. She likes that he buys her little gifts—scented soaps and chocolates, things Paul would never even notice.

Mostly, though, what she likes is that after sex, instead of rolling over and falling asleep, he gets up and goes into the kitchen. He makes her tea and an omelet while, wrapped in a sheet, she sits at the table, watching him. They read the newspaper together, watch an old movie on television, and then end up back in bed.

Hours later, Denise wakes with a start. She can't remember where she is. She looks at the sheets striped black and purple. Paul would have a heart attack if he slept on anything other than pale pastel sheets. Quickly she gets out of bed, but she can't find her underwear. It's already 2 o'clock. She has an hour to get all her errands done before she has to pick up the kids.

She is going to be late again.

This goes on all the time, says Susan Shapiro Barash, a professor of critical thinking/gender studies at Marymount Manhattan College in New York City and the author of A *Passion for More: Wives Reveal the Affairs That Make or Break Their Marriages.* In her research on female infidelity, conducted over the past 12 years, she found that about 60 percent of American women have an affair at some point in their marriages. Forty percent of these women see their affairs as escapes, and 60 percent consider their cheating indicative of larger problems in their marriages. Perhaps most shocking is that 90 percent of the cheating women said they didn't feel guilty.

What's more: Of the seven adulterous women I spoke with for this story, none are getting divorced or have experienced some major fallout because of their affairs. Many feel they are well within their rights to deceive their husbands. Denise is typical in feeling entitled to her man on the side.

Her affair started when she was barely pregnant with her second child. At the time, her husband's job wasn't going well. He wasn't making much money. He was depressed, moping around the house in a green bathrobe, feeling sorry for himself. It infuriated her. Worse, she had to support them with money she'd inherited when her father died. She didn't want to feel so angry and resentful, but the fact of it was, she did. She'd kept up her part of the bargain. She'd quit her job at the law firm where she was a paralegal, and had his children. It's not that she stopped loving Paul or her kids. There is no way she'd leave them. Her affair is just a strike against the tyranny of the never-ending piles of laundry, the PTA meetings, the to-do lists that now dictate her soccer mom days.

Thankfully for women like Denise, we no longer live in the time of Nathaniel Hawthorne's Hester Prynne. Adulterous females can no longer be identified by a scarlet letter A. Neither do they skulk around in trench coats like Catherine Deneuve's bored housewife turned whore in *Belle de Jour.* Seldom are they blessed with typical femme fatale looks, like raven hair and violet eyes. No, today's erotic infidels wear yoga pants, turtlenecks, short skirts, and sweatpants. They look like your coworker, your girlfriend, your sister, maybe even your wife.

So, what's behind the sheer tonnage of *Save Your Marriage!* and *Infidelity for Idiots* books? Given the anecdotal and research data, female infidelity is not a fad but a logical extension of female empowerment and the sexual revolution. The phenomenon is driven by both economic and psychological factors.

Today's women, who grew up with premarital sex as a given, are the equals of men in the workplace, a place statistics show to be fertile ground for extramarital affairs. The late Shirley Glass, a psychologist famous for writing a book about infidelity called *Not "Just Friends,"* posited, "Now, men and women are working together as equals, with a lot of intellectual energy and common interests. It's a combination of emotional and sexual bonds. And it's more dangerous because it creates an alternative to the marriage, rather than just a supplement."

Not only has the workplace become a venue where women are exposed to the same temptations that men have been wrestling with since office Christmas parties began; it may also create a biochemical motivation to cheat. "The allure and attraction in the workplace come from women stepping into an environment where they are actually in control and are appreciated. As their level of confidence increases, women's testosterone levels start to rise," suggests Scott Haltzman, M.D., clinical assistant professor of psychiatry and human behavior at Brown University. "This rise comes out of feelings of competitiveness, and they start to sense more sexual stirrings."

It used to be that women got older and men got richer: A woman's stock plunged, while a man's value never diminished. But that is no longer the case. Today's women are more financially independent than ever before, many choosing to keep bank accounts separate from their husbands'. And though infidelity cannot be identified as more prevalent in one class or race, it does seem that the more educated a woman is, the more easily she is able to slip out of the shackles of monogamy.

Women are taking better care of themselves, too. One need only look in the window of the neighborhood fitness center to see that today's wives are no longer willing to adopt middle-age spread and pantsuits as their mothers did. "Women are looking for physical validation," says Bonnie Eaker Weil, Ph.D., author of *Adultery: The Forgivable Sin* and a psychiatrist in private practice in New York City. "They've had babies, they are in the workplace, they still have great bodies. They are cheating the way men used to do years ago." Also like men, women who choose to step out select lovers either who look just like their husbands did before they turned paunchy or who are polar opposites of their spouses. The result is a kind of psychic splitting similar to how some men suffer from the Madonna/whore complex.

Kate, a 43-year-old architect in New York City, is happily married but likes to spice things up with bawdy e-mail.

Kate met Phillip 3 years ago, when she went back to work after her daughter, Maggie, started school. "There was a corps of people who were flying to Boston once a week and staying in a huge luxury hotel. And there was this one man, Phillip; he was very attractive, and he had this energy," she says.

INSTANT SEXPERT

Is She the One?

Complete the good-wife checklist:

• Good wives are interested in being good moms.

• Good wives have that sex trigger you want to keep pulling.

• Good wives drive like guys. Driving is a great measure of competency.

• Good wives understand how to nurture and grow your money.

• Good wives have a sense of humor (or they wouldn't have considered you).

• Good wives are not being treated on an outpatient basis for anything.

Shortly after meeting, the two started exchanging several flirtatious BlackBerry text messages a day and taking long lunches.

"He was a bad boy," she says, laughing. "He was trouble. All my
boyfriends had been bad boys. My husband was the first nice boy I'd
ever dated. You wonder, What if you could be adored every day? I'd
come back on Sunday nights, and I was really buzzed from it all."

"The lover is all about a woman's needs versus the needs of
everyone else, like her husband, children, mother, or mother-in-law. It
takes her outside that all-consuming, incredibly mundane life because
it's very much a daily grind," says Gail Wyatt, Ph.D., a professor of
psychiatry and biobehavioral science at UCLA.

Having an affair is not just about women's wanting to experience the promise of their sexual peak at a time when their marriages
may be stagnating. It's also about autonomy and choices. It's part of
finding out who they really are. Call it the dark side of feminism:
Women have been raised to believe they can have everything men
can—and on the flip side, they can behave just as badly. The difference is that women are better wired for the emotional compartmentalization and secrecy that adultery demands, explains Marymount
Manhattan College's Barash. "Women are very good at multitasking,"
she says.

Tracy is a 38-year-old advertising executive turned stay-at-home
mom. Her husband is a workaholic. She misses the sexual tension of
the workplace and is looking for something to fill that void.

Tracy has bought flowers and lit candles; she's wearing the Cos-
abella thong she bought weeks ago at the suggestion of a girlfriend
who has had several lovers. The girlfriend had told Tracy she deserved
it. After all, she's lost 10 pounds and finally cut off her hair, so she
looks years younger. She isn't sure whether her friend meant she deserved the thong or the boyfriend. Tracy has had only five partners in
her life, which, compared with her girlfriends, seems like peanuts.
She can't help wondering what she is missing.

She has dabbed perfume behind her knees and between her thighs. Last night, lying in bed, unable to sleep, she realized that she and Brian haven't had sex—real sex, not 5-minute "honey, leave me alone" courtesy sex—in more than a month. She knows she wants something more. She has tried the usual remedies. She ordered a series of soft-core porn films supposedly guaranteed to spice up your sex life. (They didn't; both she and Brian were turned off by the sheer amount of body hair on both genders.) She has a stack of how-to-drive-men-wild books stashed beneath the bed. But when Brian comes to bed, distracted, overweight, often with a folder of legal briefs, she doesn't even want him to touch her. It just feels pathetic.

Tonight all that will change. She had the nanny bathe Grace and has put the girls to bed a half hour early, so when Brian comes home at 9 o'clock, they are alone. He opens the bottle of wine she's bought and pulls off his tie. He doesn't notice the flowers or the candles or the fact that she smells like a brothel. They eat dinner, he oblivious, she in a simmering rage. He talks about work (his boss is an asshole, he gets no respect) and a squash tournament that's coming up. Then, even though he seems bored by it, she tells him about her day—taking the girls to the pediatrician, calling about a rental on the cape, having coffee with a friend at the playground. Coffee with a friend. He can't say she didn't warn him.

Her hand flits to her face. She feels her cheeks, wondering if she looks any different when she is thinking about Ben. She finds herself thinking about him all the time now. Anytime he calls to see if she and Grace are headed to the park, she gets butterflies. Like Tracy, Ben is taking time off from his career—working in finance, his wife makes three times what he did—to stay home with his daughter, who just happens to be the same age as her Grace. They met at the sandbox in the park. Grace offered his daughter a Band-Aid to eat, and the parents quickly fell into talking. Ben laughed at her jokes and joined her in bashing President Bush, something Brian would never do. They

(continued on page 188)

Profile of an Unfaithful Wife: 15 Attributes of the Woman Who Fools Around

1. She's in her thirties. Rates of infidelity start to rise among women in their midthirties after they've been married for 7 years, according to infidelity experts.

2. She works. Working women are more likely to cheat than stay-at-home moms. And they're most likely to cheat with a coworker, according to the late Shirley Glass, Ph.D., who was an expert on female infidelity. Ditto with men who cheat. It's partly an opportunity thing; we tend to love the ones we're with, according to research by Cindy Hazan, Ph.D., associate professor of human development at Cornell. But it also reflects the reality of today's office life, where intense side-by-side work forges deep connections.

3. She makes more than $75,000 a year. Same goes for men. The highly paid are more likely to cheat, according to National Opinion Research Center data—obviously because they can afford the bar tab.

4. She was married before. "Second marriages are higher in divorce and adultery than first marriages," according to marriage therapist Bonnie Eaker Weil, Ph.D.

5. One of her parents had affairs. Children of cheaters are more likely to repeat family history, says Weil.

6. She's unhappy with you. Women who say they're "not too happy" in their marriages are nearly four times as likely to have an affair as women who say their marriage is "very happy," according to a sampling of 544 adulterous adults who were polled by the National Opinion Research Center (NORC). And nearly half of all women think an affair is perfectly okay if the marriage stinks; she's just keeping it together for the kids.

7. She has a 1-year-old child. Two-thirds of wives report a significant decline in marital satisfaction around this time, according to a 6-year University of Washington study of newlywed couples.

8. She doesn't go to church or synagogue. Women who never attend religious services are 2.5 times as likely to cheat as those who attend more than once a week, according to data from the NORC survey.

9. She's watching *The Bachelorette* while you're at poker night. Couples who entered therapy after an affair reported that they had been spending less time together than typical married couples do, according to a study by David C. Atkins, Ph.D., a clinical psychologist at the Travis Research Institute in Pasadena, California. Men like to think that once they're married, they've "got that covered." Then their wives wander off with someone who makes them feel adored again.

10. She has low self-esteem. A major benefit of an affair, say women who stray, is the ego boost, according to a study by University of Texas evolutionary psychologist David M. Buss, Ph.D.

11. She's a little nutty and a little slutty. A number of studies suggest that women who tend to be narcissistic and who crave sexual variety and excitement are more likely to jump ship than women with less neurotic personality traits. Also, women who are friendly and extroverted get propositioned the most, according to a study by David P. Schmitt, Ph.D., an associate professor of psychology at Bradley University in Peoria, Illinois.

12. She's hot. In which case, face it: She's getting plenty of feelers. "Such people get used to being adored," says marriage therapist Pepper Schwartz, Ph.D., in *Everything You Know about Love and Sex Is Wrong*.

13. And getting hotter. Is she working out at Bally's? Changing salons? Buying new clothes? Enhancing her physical appearance is a top tactic of female "mate poachers," say psychologists Buss and Schmitt.

14. She wants you to wear this harness. If your wife introduces sex toys or has a favorite new position that seems outside of her usual repertoire, she may have learned from a substitute teacher, says Don-David Lusterman, Ph.D., author of *Infidelity: A Survival Guide*.

15. She's ovulating. New research by Steven Gangestad, Ph.D., at the University of New Mexico, reveals that women's sex fantasies of other men nearly double during their days of peak fertility. In other words, she's thinking about her boss on the very day he could become the father of her next child. Not that you're worried. . . .

talked about their hometowns, about road trips they'd taken cross-country and across Europe, and about the drugs they'd once done—sometimes parenthood is like being on acid, isn't it? And they complained, both of them, about their spouses in the most oblique ways. They just don't understand. . . .

Last week, he'd kissed her as they were parting. She'd turned her head at the last moment, and he'd kissed only half her mouth. Still, it was a kiss, and she couldn't stop thinking about it. She thought about telling Brian, but he would think it was a joke. No, she decided, this experience belonged to her.

That is why today, at the park, she let her hand rest on Ben's thigh, and why later, when they'd followed their girls over to the jungle gym and he stood so close behind her, she laughed nervously. Without speaking, they both moved over toward the hedge that ran along the periphery of the playground. It's okay, she thought. Nothing is happening, this is silly, it's just a kiss, and there are nannies around, other parents, the children are safe.

Hidden behind the boxwoods, he kissed her again, his hands up under her blouse, then cupping her ass. It was scary, but she thinks she'd have let him do her right there and then if they hadn't been outside like that. It was like she'd gone mad. What's wrong with her?

As Brian gets up from the table and begins clearing the plates, she tells herself that the next time she sees Ben, she is going to make sure that she hasn't shaved her legs or armpits or that she's wearing ratty underwear. This way, maybe she can keep herself from taking her pants off.

For some women, this postchildren, second-career-on-the-horizon moment in their lives is when they realize they have sailed into terra incognita on the map that society has drawn for them. They hadn't planned on this desire for more. From the peak of experience, they can survey the marital terrain for what it is. Sure, there are the occasionally staggering vistas, but it is also flat for miles and miles, and like sexual conquistadores with a fleet of fast ships, these women thirst for riches and discovery.

Witness the collective nerve that Laura Kipnis's *Against Love* pinched among women of a certain age when it was published in 2003. In the provocative and highly entertaining polemic against marriage, the author scrutinizes the "work ethic" couples now adopt in regard to their relationships. Kipnis writes, "When monogamy becomes labor, when desire is organized contractually, with accounts kept and fidelity extracted like labor from employees, with marriage a domestic factory policed by means of rigid shop-floor discipline designed to keep the wives and husbands and domestic partners of the world choke-chained to the status quo machinery—is this really what we mean by a 'good relationship'?"

For women who wake up to find themselves trapped in a "domestic factory," taking a lover coincides with figuring out what their sexual and emotional needs really are.

"There is something to that glow," Tracy told me a few weeks after messing around in the park. "Every time you get that phone call from that person, you think about what you are giving up, or are missing out on, or were meant to have. I wonder, Can you be defined as being happily married and have an affair?" That is the big question.

The answer appears to be deeply embedded in our personality types. For narcissistic Don Juans (and their female equivalents), it can be very difficult to wean themselves from the thrill of the chase, particularly if it's a pattern established in adolescence, says Don-David Lusterman, Ph.D., author of *Infidelity: A Survival Guide* and founder of the family counseling program at Hofstra University.

Cathy, a 38-year-old from Seattle, has been married for 10 years but likes to steal away with a stranger to keep things fresh.

Cathy and her husband, Lloyd, have, by her admission, a great sex life, and they rarely fight. They go out a lot and socialize with the same group of friends.

Cathy's life is good, even great, but still there are times when all she wants is to be the wild child of her teenage years. "Because no matter how much you work at it, how many dates you make, or how much you dress up or role-play, the fact is, you know each other so well. There is no mystery. After 10 years, there's no thrill," she says.

So, sometimes at one of their big, boozy parties, when no one seems to be paying attention, she likes to sneak away and fool around with one of her guests. Cheating keeps her life from sinking into the rut of familiarity. It keeps her desire and imagination piqued. Cathy also insists that this heightened level of sexual energy translates into more action in the bedroom for her husband. Cathy has no interest in getting involved with someone long term—it's too dangerous and threatening to her marriage. Instead, she will sneak off to a bathroom with another man the way a nonsmoker will bum a cigarette at a party. She is the embodiment of what Samuel Johnson was talking about in his tale of the Abyssinian prince Rasselas when he wrote, "Marriage has many pains, but celibacy has no pleasures."

Like Cathy, Susan (a 37-year-old mother-to-be in New York City) isn't looking for a long-term lover. She's merely looking for the other. Instead of the sensitive guy she is making a life with, she craves rough trade. "Real turn-on sex is pretty animalistic," she says. "It goes against what we are trying to build at home with the man who has now become the nurturer and the foot rubber. Besides, an 18-year-old skate dude living with eight dudes is not going to threaten my relationship with my husband."

Gwen, 47, has been married for 25 years and lives in a suburb of New York. She's had several lovers over the years and has no plans to stop.

Gwen belongs to a book group that meets for dinner at a

different restaurant each month. This way, no one has to cook and no one gets stuck with the dishes. Plus, it gives everyone an excuse to get out of the house. The waiter who serves them is a pale, dark-haired man with full lips and two golden hoops in his left ear. He wears his jeans cinched low. The women giggle, admiring his ass as he walks away. Inevitably, as discussion of the novel du jour fades and the red wine and Mojitos begin to loosen tongues, the conversation turns to lovers: Who has them, and who doesn't? It is no secret that Gwen's husband, whom she married at 22, is not kind and drinks too much. Seeing other men fulfills her need for intimacy and provides her with a temporary escape from a bad marriage.

Gwen has had several lovers: One was a friend of her husband's; another was a man she'd met through a colleague at her public relations firm. "Ideally," Gwen says, "I don't think a woman should have a relationship out of the marriage. I think other women are influenced by my having had an affair—now they want one. I had no idea I could have such influence over other people."

In a Hollywood melodrama, a cheating spouse is almost always punished for her sins. The adulteress's toddler chases an errant playground ball into traffic, or her husband goes crazy and bludgeons her lover. But life does not come with these cathartic cause-and-effect scenarios. None of the women I spoke with for this story felt their marriages were irreparably damaged because of their affairs. However, just because we live in an increasingly guilt-free society doesn't mean that actions don't have consequences.

"At the onset (of the adulterous relationship), you have the woman feeling more energy, more sense of elation on a day-to-day basis, but almost inevitably, that elation will disappear eventually, and it will become a real drain on her," says Lusterman. This drain will ultimately affect the people she didn't want to hurt. She'll become depressed but won't be able to talk about the loss of her lover, creating further distance between her and her husband. Worse still, she may not be aware of the message she is subliminally sending her kids or of how this message will be translated into behavior when they grow up and create families of their own.

"My parents both cheated," says Susan of her childhood object lesson in family values. She doesn't use their shortcomings to rationalize why she can't help sabotaging a picture-perfect life by having sex with strangers. To her, it's just a part of who she is. "They both experienced digressions. I think Dad was definitely worse. My mother just cheated in retaliation," she says, adding, "I just know that I did inherit it."

Far Away, Far from Bad

An expert debunks the long-distance myth

FORGET WHAT YOUR BUDDIES TELL YOU. Long-distance relationships work. The temptation? A myth. The lack of visits? Easy to overcome. The insane phone bills? Probably no more than you would spend together, anyway.

What's really important, according to Gregory Guldner, M.D., the author of *Long Distance Relationships: The Complete Guide* and the director of the Center for the Study of Long Distance Relationships, is that both people, like any couple, stay involved in each other's lives. We asked Guldner for his advice on how to keep the separation from tearing you apart. He shares how to get past the myths and learn the secrets that will make it work.

Let's start with the hard numbers: How many U.S. residents are in long-distance relationships?

All together, about 13 million people. Our best estimate is that somewhere between 2.5 and 3 million people are in long-distance marriages. That's 3 to 7 percent of all marriages. And probably another 10 million dating couples. Between 1999 and 2002, which is the latest data out there, long-distance marriages increased by 385,000. We've become quite a mobile society, and as people travel for business and use the Internet more, they tend to meet others further away. Plus, we have troops all over the world right now.

What are the misconceptions about long-distance relationships?
The biggest one is that they don't work. Men in particular have (perpetuated) that myth. There's a whole field that focuses on the end of relationships that shows women tend to blame the breakup on something within the relationship itself. Men like to look outside the relationship. And that's what happens with long-distance ones. It's so tempting to blame the distance. Yet if you look at the studies, that just isn't true. The couples who break up would probably break up anyway, regardless of the distance.

If you look at the rates of breakups or divorces, you see there isn't any increase for those who live further apart. If you look at quality, you see they have not found any difference between separated couples and those living close by.

Another big myth is that couples in long-distance relationships are more likely to have an affair; it's not true. In studies, frequency of face-to-face visits or phone calls also had nothing to do with the quality of the relationship or success rate. That's good because people can't control that—because either they don't have the money or, in the case of a military separation, they don't have control over the visits.

The other myth is that men do better in a separation than woman. Men actually do worse. Compared with women, men tend to deal with long-distance relationships with more physical symptoms and more psychological symptoms: minor depression, trouble sleeping, difficulty concentrating. At the beginning of a separation, they may become quite anxious. For some, that causes gastrointestinal problems, nausea, upset stomach.

Does that get easier?
No, unfortunately. The separation symptoms are the same for the first as well as for the 40th separation, and it's the same for civilians and

for the military. It's acting as a reflex. You need to have a plan to deal with issues of anxiety and depression because they won't just go away.

What should you do?

First, stay optimistic. When we looked at the effectiveness of various coping strategies, the only one that came up helpful is to think positively. The research shows that long-distance relationships work just as well, that they're not as likely to fall victim to affairs, and that they're often the best alternative if your options are giving up a career goal, moving, or not dating. Remember, you chose to do this rather than to break up. Be positive about it.

If a guy looked, he'd probably find lots of advantages to long-distance relationships. Can you name a few?

There's the novelty issue. Close couples tend to take each other for granted; it happens with practically every couple. Separated couples have that honeymoon session. They rediscover each other whenever they're face-to-face. And if they're apart more than 2 weeks, the sex when they get together is like the sex at the beginning of their relationship: heated and wild.

Another big advantage? Compartmentalization. When apart from their partners, they're very focused on what they're doing, be it work or school. They can be very productive. One of our studies showed that students in college who are in long-distance relationships tend to get better grades than those in relationships that are close.

Plus, you don't have to call that you'll be late.

Or ask, "Is it okay that I go meet the guys?" It satisfies that need to be autonomous. Then it's like flipping a switch. When you're together, you're very focused on each other, and you're very intimate. It's a nice balance between intimacy and autonomy, but it's not a long-term solution.

What's the biggest issue that sabotages these relationships?

Learning how to be intimate long-distance. I think that destroys most long-distance relationships. The couple just stops feeling like they're part of each other's world. Intimacy entails sharing your day-to-day details. That may seem silly. You want to express how much you care, so you say "I love you so much" and hang up the phone. And then you think, Wow, I don't feel any closer.

How do you rediscover that intimacy?

If you can't talk to each other every day, keep a diary or keep track of events to relearn what intimacy is.

It's not conscious, but in a traditional relationship, you tend to chat casually while one's doing the laundry, the other's watching TV. It's a very nonchalant thing that helps with intimacy. In a long-distance relationship, because you are on the phone, you are very focused on talking with each other. It's so formal that it reinforces the fact that you're apart.

We suggest a hands-free wireless phone because you can do laundry and talk to your partner. And a hands-free phone mimics the way traditional couples interact.

Are there other telephone issues long-distance couples usually have?

Studies show that on the telephone, people don't trust the other person as much. If you're arguing about important issues, the telephone is a dangerous toy. It can make things worse. You're missing the subtle cues you get when seeing the person face-to-face, those clues that what they said wasn't meant to attack you.

But if you can't be face-to-face, how do you get around that?

Written letters are a very good way to help with the relationship. The couples who stayed together each wrote twice as much as those who didn't. We've seen that in a couple of studies.

The best use of e-mail is to help with that issue of staying in touch with day-to-day things.

For more intimate messages, it's good to send a handwritten letter. When it traveled all that way to you, it gets a more emotional feeling. People in focus groups hold on to those letters, and an important part of that is that it was in your partner's hands.

What other steps can you take to keep the relationship healthy?
Don't sidestep arguments. One of the typical problems is that people don't really want to rock the boat, so to speak. They've shown that couples in long-distance relationships argue less, even when you take into account that they interact less than those in traditional relationships. In a 2-day weekend, you've got a choice. You can ignore it— you'll be there for only a couple days. Or you can bring it up and risk ruining the whole weekend.

But relationships move forward through conflict. Progress is based on discovering problems and deciding if these are issues you can work through or if this is a deal breaker. Instead, the problems get bigger and bigger.

Our research showed that a long-distance couple who will break up will do so at a slower rate than a couple living geographically close. If they're ultimately going to break up anyway, they'll cling together longer because they just don't address these issues.

That's also why couples who do break up tend to cling to each other longer. They don't have that constant reminder of those bad things, and their misery is prolonged.

So, couples avoid fighting to stay together, but they won't stay together if they avoid fighting. It's a catch-22.
Yes. Every relationship has problems, but if you don't deal with them, they'll get dragged out. Some couples don't want to talk about the rules in terms of dating others, or even hanging out with others. It

doesn't matter an awful lot what people decide, even if they decide to date other people. All that matters is that it's discussed.

In our study, we found that 30 percent of couples who discussed ground rules broke up in a 6-month to 1-year period, which is the same breakup rate as those in a traditional relationship. In those who didn't discuss this, 70 percent broke up. That's more than twice the rate.

Many friends in long-distance relationships have told me that their weekends together rarely matched expectations. Why is that?
When apart from each other, you tend to look at your partner in the best possible terms. It's almost universal that people idealize the other. We think one reason long-distance relationships don't break up more is that the partners tend to focus on all the great things.

The only drawback is that if you idealize your partner and you think it's going to be the most wonderful weekend, you will be disappointed. When things don't go absolutely perfect, that's a good sign. You're beginning to see each other as real people and not as ideal partners.

A lot of couples in our focus groups tell us they have trouble knowing where the relationship is—are we okay, are we not okay—and they base that decision on the weekend. So if they had a bad weekend, they think the whole relationship isn't doing well. You need to expect that disappointment.

To go back to relearning intimacy, how can couples stay sexually connected?
I'll preface this with my obvious caveat that sexuality is not always important to all relationships, often for religious reasons. Sexuality often plays an important role in many relationships and in mental health. We know it's a good buffer. If couples are under a lot of stress and they have a good sexual relationship, they tend to show stress less than those who don't have a good sexual relationship.

Overall, people in long-distance relationships say their sex lives are great. In studies on sexual intimacy, people in such relationships report that it's equal to or better than those in geographically close relationships.

When I look at sexuality in long-distance relationships, I break it into two categories: sexuality during reunion and the long-distance sex. That can mean through the phone, but also now, with Internet capabilities and wireless phone, people are getting creative. The sex during reunions is typically great. It's that honeymoon period.

Speaking of phone sex, is it a staple of long-distance relationships?
We don't know the numbers, but it's probably at the 85 to 90 percent range that have some sort of sexual encounter on the phone. The phone sex issue we come up with is that people don't feel comfortable talking about sex. People are very anxious about saying the actual words involved. They're the same people who don't talk dirty during intercourse. We recommend the book *The Fine Art of Erotic Talk* by Bonnie Gabriel. It was meant for couples who are together, but it's great for couples who are apart. It can make the telephone connection a little more erotic.

If someone is really uncomfortable self-pleasuring—and it's probably the woman—it makes them more frustrated with the relationship. They'll feel unsatisfied sexually and more frustrated with the fact that they're separated.

What can a guy do to make his girlfriend more comfortable?
First, talk about what the issue is. If it's religious, that's tricky. You just have to work with other issues. Oftentimes, it's someone's perception that the genital area is dirty and that you just don't touch yourself.

Ask what it is that makes the person feel uncomfortable. Is she uncomfortable when her partner touches her? Is she uncomfortable with body massages? The next step is, when the couple gets together, to have the comfortable partner put his hand over his partner's hand and gradually move it away. Others prefer to take it on as a solo project. Then you should ask what part of touching yourself makes you uncomfortable. Sometimes they can touch themselves over their clothes and move them down to not having clothes on.

Generally, if they're uncomfortable with self-pleasuring, they'll be less interested in phone sex, so to speak, and it removes one possibility to have a sexual encounter when they're separated.

If people aren't comfortable with phone sex, what are other alternatives to stay sexually connected?
Write down fantasies; send Polaroids. But be careful with that because if the relationship ends, that stuff can end up on the Internet.

How do military couples handle the forced separation?
The reaction depends on where you're deployed. The key component that makes it different isn't just that we're separated but also that we may never see each other again. Plus, you can't pick up and call on the cell phone. There's a much higher rate of major depression: 1 in 5 in military spouses. The flip side is that at least for those in active duty, the military has a good support system.

Looking at the big picture, can lessons we learn from long-distance relationships be applied to traditional relationships?
From a sexuality standpoint, distance helps you focus on what you hear. We tend to be very focused visually, especially men. There's a separate component of sexuality that's auditory and that involves what sounds you and your partner make. In long-distance relationships, especially with phone sex, you develop an appreciation of those sounds.

Also, it's easy to take each other for granted. When you're separated, you remember the excitement you have and how in love you feel when you first get together again.

Should we follow the separated couples and take a break from our relationships?
There's a school of thought in marriage therapy that does pull the couple apart for a while. A small vacation away from each other isn't bad. Remember you have to take care of yourself. You need time to see your buddies. You need to feel comfortable to be intimate. And you need time to focus on each other.

Getting personal, have you been in any long-distance relationships?
Yes. I've been in at least five long-distance relationships that have lasted more than a year. My last long-distance relationship lasted four years. Now she's my wife.

QUICKIES

G Marks the Spot

All women have 7G-spots. Your mission: Join the search party. "It's a lot easier for a woman to find her G-spot with the help of a partner," says sex therapist Judith Seifer, Ph.D. Try this reconnaissance route: During foreplay, have her lie on her back, and insert your longest finger into her love shack, slowly running it along the front vaginal wall (the side toward her belly). In this palm-up position, curl your finger toward you as if you were motioning her to "come here" (pun intended). You should feel a knot of muscle the size of a nickel, about 3 to 4 inches above the opening. That's her G-spot: the place where all her pelvic nerves fuse together. "Once you've found it with your finger, she'll be more receptive to feeling stimulation by you during intercourse," Seifer says.

Sniff for Sex

Researchers are currently testing a nasal spray that will produce an erection in 30 minutes. Made up of a water-based solution of the naturally occurring hormone alpha-MSH, the spray is designed to trigger a brain response that in turn increases bloodflow to the genitals. Possible side effects include a tan—another reason sniffers might get more sex. Palatin Technologies expects to submit the spray, called PT-141, for FDA approval in 2006.

Recipe for Romance

When you're cooking a romantic dinner, there are so many potential pitfalls—singed eyebrows, scalded crotch. We recommend oven mitts and these tips, courtesy of Doug Veith, coauthor of *Win Her with Dinner*.

TIME IT WELL. The third date is when the good stuff often happens, says Veith, so it's smart to be close to home. But anniversaries and Fridays are also good times.

AVOID SURPRISES. Always clear the proposed meal with the proposed woman ahead of time, says Veith. Make sure she doesn't have any allergy or diet issues.

IMPROVE THE SETTING. If you have a dining room, great. Otherwise, dress up any flat surface with a tablecloth, cloth napkins, and matching salad and dinner plates. To upgrade the setting, Veith suggests sunflowers—an innocent and safe flower—and unscented candles.

PLAY MUSIC. Try to pair the song selection with your menu. For a classic American dinner, such as New York strip steak, try Billie Holiday. For an Italian supper, spin Paolo Conte. Good Charlotte doesn't go with anything. But the book has plenty of other pairing suggestions.

DON'T FORGET DESSERT. At the least, she'll leave with a good taste in her mouth.

Blonde versus Brunette

Say you're faced with the unfair dilemma of choosing between a sultry, brown-haired beauty or a gorgeous, flaxen-headed hottie. (The redhead already left with your buddy.) What would you do? To help you out, we compiled the research and consulted some of the brightest minds on the matter.

LOOKS. In a recent survey on the world's most beautiful women by askmen.com, 10 were blondes, nine were brunettes, and there was one redhead. (Isn't there always?) The reason blondes led the field? "Golden hair brings out the color of the eyes and makes teeth look whiter," says Natalia Ilyin, a psychologist and the author of *Blonde Like Me*.

Advantage: Blonde

FIDELITY. Men typically want brunettes as wives. A test by anthropologist Hans Juergens revealed that personal ads placed by brunettes looking for husbands received twice as many responses as those posted by blondes. "Blondes tend to be bigger risk-takers and more likely to want to play around," says psychologist Tony Fallone, Ph.D.

Advantage: Brunette

SUGAR-MAMA POTENTIAL. Research has shown that brunettes have more job security, says Fallone. His research on hair color and psychology also found that men perceive brunettes as more intelligent and reliable, while blondes are considered flaky.

Advantage Brunette

Winner: Brunette. See what brown can do for you.

STAY CLOSE

Business trips can end at home with a warm bed, a cold shoulder, or lukewarm indifference. Improve your odds by listening to Rikki Klieman, whose marriage to Bill Bratton features more frequent departures than LAX.

He's the Los Angeles police chief who used to globe-hop as a security consultant; she's a trial attorney, a Court TV anchor, and the author of the memoir *Fairy Tales Can Come True*. Klieman's advice to ensure happy homecomings:

- Buy some cards—sappy, goofy, whatever works—sign them, and slap on stamps before you leave. Mail them one at a time from your destination. You're so thoughtful!
- Give her your itinerary and phone numbers. Schedule two calls a day.

• Explain the precise reason for the trip. Let her know which days you'll be under the gun so she'll understand any communication blackouts.

• Never end a call with an argument; 5 bad minutes can create 5 bad days. Be willing to compromise, since the person waiting at home needs to feel secure.

• Buy something. It takes only a moment and shows thought—even if it's just a trinket.

• Back home, go on a date. Just the two of you; no kids, no friends. Get reacquainted.

ASK THE GIRL
NEXT DOOR
The honest truth about women
from our lovely neighbor

Laying and Lying

What are some of the signs that a woman is cheating on her husband or boyfriend?   —ANONYMOUS

Did you see the movie *Unfaithful*? If not, rent the DVD—it'll make all of your past failed relationships look like a walk in the park. The wayward wife, played by Diane Lane, shows all the classic signs.

If she's two-timing you, a woman will start turning down your invitations, claiming she's too busy with friends, hair appointments, or work to spend time with you. She'll be less talkative and more distracted but won't have a convincing explanation when you ask her why. She'll stop initiating sex—and when you try, she'll act uncomfortable and hesitant. She may also be spending a suspicious amount of time on her cell phone out of earshot, or sending e-mails late at night. When you call her, she'll sound vaguely disappointed that it's you. Look out for new dresses, shoes, and lingerie that you never see her wear. Is she glowing and happy and giggly, yet not directing any of that positive energy toward you? Then the source of that glow might be another man.

Save the Wails

How are we really supposed to know you're having an orgasm?

—DOUG, VIA E-MAIL

I've read enough of those "how to tell if she's faking it" articles to know there is an undeniable list of physical events that always occur when a woman is climaxing (increased wetness, vaginal muscle spasms, erect nipples, redder lips)—but these can be pretty hard to detect when you're thrusting at top speed or wearing earmuffs made out of your girlfriend's thighs. So I recommend that you ask the direct, but always welcome, question "Did you come?" instead of trying to play Sherlock Holmes during a shagfest. Might she lie? Yes. (According to one survey, 44 percent of women have faked it at least once.)

Stopped in the Name of Love

My fiancée wants to stop having sex 4 months before the wedding so our wedding night will be more "special." Is this common?

—PAUL, VIA E-MAIL

A new bride wanting her wedding night to be special? Yeah, that's rather common. Giving up sex for 120 days to accomplish it? Not so much. That said, she's not trying to torture you—she just wants you to yearn for her like a shipwreck victim yearns for a passing ocean liner. That way, when you're ripping off her bodice with the teeth she insisted you have whitened ("for the photos, darling"), you'll both feel as if you've married the sexiest person on the planet. Manipulative? Yes. Effective? You betcha.

She's also hoping that abstaining will make her feel more like the virgin she's supposed to be on her wedding day, which is kind of sweet, right? A recent poll by *Cosmopolitan* magazine and TheKnot.com revealed that 28 percent of women abstain from sex for a few days before their wedding, 18 percent impose the no-nookie rule for a few weeks, and 12 percent refrain from doing it for several months. Four months is pushing it. Suggest a compromise:

She cuts it back to 1 month, and you won't pitch a tent during the ceremony.

Reassure, Ring

**I want to propose to my girlfriend, but I'm not sure if she'll say yes.
Any way I can tell for sure?**   —JUDAH, BROOKLYN, NEW YORK

First, understand this isn't about you. Or "us." It's about her—more
specifically, how she feels about the concept of marriage. Take my
friend Maria. Her relationship with John was so unstable it threatened
to take hostages. But when John went down on one knee in front of
the Angel of the Water fountain in New York's Central Park, a shocked
Maria paused and then screamed "Yes!" Sure, she had doubts, but
she's always believed that marriage strengthens a couple—that it gives
them a secure environment, and a heap of motivation, to learn how to
be better friends and lovers. Another friend of mine, Monica, was in a
similarly torqued relationship with a man she was crazy in love with.
When he handed her a diamond after hiking with her to a beautiful
spot on a lake, she responded with "I think we should wait." Monica
believes marriage is something you do after you iron out all the relationship wrinkles—and not a moment sooner. So listen to your girlfriend's comments about marriage.

Is it the tape you break at the end of the marathon, or the bottle
of Gatorade you down halfway, that makes the rest of the race a
breeze? Now you know how she'll make her decision.

Properly Groomed

I want to make our wedding night perfect. Suggestions?
—DAVID, NEW MEXICO

Perfect? You're lucky if you even get it on after such a long, exhausting day. Your M.O. should be "slow and passionate." Gently help
her out of her dress, kissing each bit of skin that becomes available.
Admire the delicate lace lingerie that's sure to be underneath. Tell her
she's beautiful at least 10 times—and a few more times after that.
Move your hands, tongue, and lips slowly but firmly over her entire

body no matter what specific action you're performing. This definitely isn't the time to try anything new or kinky—instead, treat her to all the moves that you know she loves (hell, they're probably the reason she married you). As for prep, light the requisite candles and turn on some quiet and sexy music, like African blues king Ali Farka Toure. Make sure the CD player is on repeat; you don't want the music to stop at a crucial moment. And most important of all, go easy on the hooch at the reception; otherwise, your little groomsman might not make it to the altar.

HOT MONOGAMY

S ex can be really boring. That's right, we said it. Once you're getting it on a regular basis, sex is no different from any luxury overindulged. Wear a crisp Armani suit one day and you'll feel like George Clooney. Wear it 365 days straight and it gets old faster than a *Facts of Life* rerun.

So, how do you keep your sex life from feeling like bad comedy in syndication? Easy—you mix things up. In this section, you'll discover the new, odd, and somewhat surprising ways you can keep things hot. Give it a read; then get to work. We promise your love life will go from *Gimme a Break* to *Real Sex* faster than you can say "I love Tootie."

11 Ways to Spice Up the Sex When You're in Bed

New things to try when the sex gets tired.

—BY THE EDITORS OF *MEN'S HEALTH* MAGAZINE

1. Suck on a mint. If your partner sucks on a breath mint before giving you oral sex, it'll be more pleasurable for you. The peppermint oil in some mints can cause a mild irritation that brings a flushed, warm sensation to the skin.

2. Eat some fruit beforehand. If your partner objects to giving you oral sex because, well, it just plain tastes bad, an apple a day might help. High in natural sugars, fruit reportedly blesses men with sweeter seminal fluid.

3. Create a fantasy box. Take an empty tissue box and make it your "fantasy box." Write five secret sexual desires on individual slips of paper, have your partner do the same, then deposit them in the box. (Hold off on the ménage à trois for a while.) Take turns drawing one whenever you make love.

4. Play BattleStrip. It's Saturday night. You're snowed in with nothing but old board games and two warm bodies. That's all you need to score.

MONOPOLY: Make up your own Community Chest and Chance cards.

TWISTER: You've already thrown down the plastic tarp. Now make it slippery.

BATTLESTRIP: Draw your clothes, and hers, on two paper grids. You say E-5, she loses her bra. She says F-7, you unleash the torpedo.

5. Hum during oral sex. Anytime you touch the skin with something vibrating, you transmit sensation to a wider area than you would through simple stroking. So relax your lips (think Mick Jagger) and hum a tune (maybe "Brown Sugar") as you bring the outermost portion of your kisser in contact with her vaginal lips.

6. Lick, then blow. By licking her nipples, private parts, and neck, then blowing on the wet patches you've created, you can generate a sexy tingle that'll drive your woman wild. To make her head spin even more, use alcohol. It evaporates more quickly than water or saliva, producing a greater cooling effect.

7. Hide the honey. You're blindfolded; she hides a dab of honey somewhere on her body. You try to find it—using only your tongue.

8. Lose the tie. A necktie is the one article of men's clothing that women love most. The way the silk feels against her skin, the way it smells after being tied around your neck all day. Mmm. So take it off and rub it against her skin or, even better, use it to cover her eyes. She won't be able to anticipate where or when your next kiss or touch is coming, so every touch will feel more intense.

9. Turn on a black light. A black light positioned near the bed really helps start things cooking. It gives naked bodies a sexy-looking tan without either of you having to destroy your skin by baking in the sun. They're available at any home store.

10. Play the alphabet game. Make capital letters with your tongue very slowly on her clitoris. See if you can make it to M.

11. Shower her with flowers. Put flower petals on top of the blades of a ceiling fan. Turn it on when she lies down.

The Sex You Deserve

A few how-tos to get you in the mood

BY JENNIFER BENJAMIN

H**AVING TROUBLE** getting your woman (or yourself) excited about sex? Try these tricks to coax the animal inside both of you out of their caves.

- **STOP AT A DRUGSTORE.** Buy a decorative gift bag and stuff it with as many bath products as you can find (bubble bath, sponge, shampoo, lotion). Attach a note that says, "Tonight, your body is in my hands." Flash your eyebrows, wink, and head for the bath. (She'll faint with pleasure, especially if you've cleaned the tub, too.)
- **GET INTO A FIGHT.** Think about it: Makeup sex is the best. When you fight, anger drives up testosterone in both men and women. If you go to bed with increased testosterone and agitation, the sex drive is going to be stronger. Of course, you don't really want to fight. But you can reenact fighting—and the emotions that go along with it—without hurting each other. Try something that will create a little physical tension between the two of you. Like miniature golf. Or any game that's just a little competitive. If all else fails, initiate a pillow fight. It starts with her hair flying and her breasts moving, and even gets her

gasping a little for breath. There's something very sexual about that.

• **GO TO A VIDEO STORE** and rent the first movie you ever watched together at a theater. She'll be so touched you remember that she won't even notice that this gift cost you

$2.99. Make popcorn, drink wine, and see if that old stretch-your-arm-around-her-shoulder trick still works.

• **PICK HER UP AFTER WORK,** but don't tell her where you're going. Then take her on a tour of places that are special to the two of you—the bar where you had your first date, the park where you dropped the L-bomb, the parking lot where you dropped your virginity. At each spot, reminisce about your relationship. Memories are almost as good for her as ESPN Classic is for you.

25 Fun Things to Do with a Woman

Stuck for something to do this evening, this weekend, this year?
May we suggest a few adventures that will kick-start
your relationship and lead to a time of romance?

BY CHRIS CONNOLLY

H**ERSHEY'S SYRUP,** whipped cream, and a Catwoman
mask. Yes, yes, we were thinking the same thing: Nothing beats sweet
sex and a woman who purrs. But what if you're still trying to get to
the sex part of your relationship, or you're trying to get more of it and
in increasingly adventuresome locations/positions? Well, that's where
the fun comes in.

"Ultimately, fun is the best aphrodisiac," says Paul Joannides, author of *The Guide to Getting It On!* "Quit looking for sexy and look
for fun instead—and you'll end up having more sex." We like the way
this guy thinks. That's why we brainstormed these adventures (with
some help from sex experts and our female friends). To get more sex.
For you. Call it our little community-service project.

1. TAKE HER TO A BALL GAME. Doesn't matter if it's major league,
minor league, or even high school ball. "I often recommend that my
couples go to a baseball game," says Howard Markman, Ph.D., coauthor of *12 Hours to a Great Marriage* and a psychologist at the University of Denver. "You sit close together, you're out in the sun, and it
gives you time to talk as friends." Of course, under no circumstances
should you go out and buy Tigers tickets! So, in the interest of our

Detroit-based readership, there are 24 more things on our list you're sure to enjoy together.

2. CLIMB A VOLCANO. Add some hot to your relationship. Molten-volcano hot. There's something about remote, dangerous places that sets the scene for romance. And few places are as remote or dangerous as the mouth of a live volcano. One of the best is in Villarrica, in south-central Chile. Expect an arduous guided climb of 8 hours, but at the end, your passions will be inflamed by the sight of all that hot, gooey lava. Then ski back down. See chile-travel.com/solnieve.htm for more information. And for a closer-to-home location, visit Mount Capulin, an inactive volcano in New Mexico, where you can actually climb inside the cone.

3. GO TO BEVERLY HILLS. And go big. A weekend spent glittering beside the glitterati at Raffles L'Ermitage in Beverly Hills doesn't come cheap—it's an "if you have to ask, you can't afford it" deal—but there's just no substitute. If you can separate yourself from your bed (with sheets spun by virgin Egyptian silk moths fed truffles, champagne, and manna), you can check out L'Ermitage's sumptuous amenities: The spa, salon, and pool are beyond compare, and the menu at Jaan, the hotel's humble restaurant, is highlighted by a $45 salad. Ouch. Yum!

4. TAKE HER SHOPPING ... BUT YOU PICK THE CLOTHES. Men don't hate shopping because of the money. It's the sitting on the boyfriend couch at Ann Taylor that we don't like. But what guy wouldn't be enthused about a mall trip if he knew that every 2 minutes a beautiful woman would pop by to model a sexy outfit he'd selected? If you agree to buy, she'll agree to model.

5. GET NAKED! Pour peppermint schnapps in her belly button. Sip it. Then kiss her breasts and blow on the spots you kissed. The peppermint schnapps and air will cause a cool sensation and heighten arousal, says Ava Cadell, Ph.D., a sex therapist and the author of *12 Steps to Everlasting Love*. And do some shopping at adult-toy online sites and at the grocery store. There's a whole world of flavors and textures out there to play with. Once you get past the headlong plunge to sex, you'll ask yourself what the hurry was, anyway. Delayed pleasures remain the most gratifying ones, especially where her body is concerned.

6. DRIVE THE PACIFIC COAST HIGHWAY IN A CONVERTIBLE. This drive—arguably the most spectacular in the country—offers stunning scenery, plenty of things to explore, and stop-offs at major destinations like San Francisco, Los Angeles, Yosemite, and San Diego. The PCH is a combination of U.S. 101 and California Route 1. Start in San Diego and take 101 North, which dips along the Pacific Ocean to L.A. Then proceed through Rodeo Drive, Beverly Hills, and Mission Santa Barbara. Stop at Hearst Castle, one of the nation's largest historic-house museums, to check out the breathtaking overlooks (800-444-4445 for information). After the castle, continue heading up the rugged coast through Monterey and then east into the Sierra Nevada. Take some time to admire Yosemite's cliffs and alpine peaks, and finish your trip at the sea in San Francisco.

7. TAKE A HOME PREGNANCY TEST. Test positive. Freak out. Call your parents. Go shopping for baby clothes. Buy a baby-names book. Eliminate Britney and Ashton as options. Start looking at colleges. . . .

8. RUN A MARATHON. Training for a race together is a crafty way to get in shape, spend time as a couple, and stay motivated. You'll have someone to talk to during those tedious long runs, you'll push each other, and you'll have to answer to your partner if you skip a workout.

Visit runnersworld.com for training schedules and a calendar of marathons. And if the mere act of running 26.2 miles isn't exciting enough, choose an exotic location—like, say, China. The Great Wall Marathon is every May. Kathy Loper Events (kathyloperevents.com) offers 7-, 9-, 10-, and 17-night packages from $1,690 to $3,350.

9. SHOOT EACH OTHER OUT OF THE SKY. Go to aircombatusa.com and find a location near you where you and your girl can fly dueling fighter jets. Take out your unresolved relationship issues while trying to blow each other to smithereens from the cockpits of SIAI Marchetti SF260s. For real. These are not simulated flights. Loser buys dinner. Hope that it's her—this little date will cost $2,000.

10. DANCE! Turn dancing into dirty dancing with an Audi-Oh vibrator, which pulsates to the speed and intensity of whatever beat is playing. Have your lady wear the discreet harness with butterfly vibe underneath her panties. Then bump and grind to throbbing music at a club, or as you play deejay at home. This is one remote you won't fight over ($80, babeland.com).

11. PLAY IN THE SAND. Run up the 750-foot dunes at the Great Sand Dunes National Monument and Preserve in southern Colorado (nps.gov/grsa). Roll down. Roll around.

12. BUILD SOMETHING FOR YOUR HOME. Home improvement demonstrates a commitment to making something you share more beautiful, requiring tools like communication, teamwork, and glue guns. "Couples come together and really communicate, sometimes for the first time in years," says Paige Davis, host of TLC's *Trading Spaces*, in which couples swap homes and redecorate. "I've seen romances rekindled." If demolition isn't for you, focus on projects that require artistry instead of sledgehammers. The Web site kitguy.com sells the means to make everything from birdhouses to porch swings and in-house saunas. But whatever you build, remember, "The key to fun is to try new things and forget about making mistakes," says Davis. Screwups can always be fixed.

13. DO WHATEVER SHE WANTS TO DO—AND LIKE IT! The happiest couples are those who can find enjoyment in sacrifice, according to a study in the *Journal of Marriage and Family* that tracked 73 couples over 13 years. "Taking pleasure in your partner's happiness enhances mutual satisfaction," says Howard Markman, Ph.D., a psychologist at the University of Denver and the coauthor of *12 Hours to a Great Marriage*. "Find out what your partner really wants to do (even shopping for curtains), make it happen, and enjoy it. It'll save you thousands in therapy." Ideas: Massage her scalp. She'll love having your hands in her hair. Or get side-by-side massages at a spa, or sign up to take a partner massage class. When you get home, jump jointly into the shower. There's nothing sexier than washing your woman's hair. Except having her wash yours.

14. CRASH THE POOL AT A LUXURY RESORT . . . because nothing's more fun than being bad.

15. GO DIVING IN SIPADAN. Never heard of it? Neither has anyone else. That's why Peter Greenberg, *Men's Health* Travel Detective, recommends it as one of the world's greatest dive spots. Located off the northeast coast of Borneo, Sipadan is Malaysia's only oceanic island. Encompassing a tiny 30 acres, this place is orgasmic for divers, featuring a spectacular and precipitous reef wall that plunges more than 1,900 feet. Getting there is part of the adventure. First, you fly to the capital of Sabah, Kota Kinabalu. Then you connect to Tawau. Then you drive to Semporna. Then you hire a catamaran to take you to the island. Exotic! Start planning now at borneo.org/ajwt.

16. SERENADE HER. Actually, pay a street musician to do it. Slip the corner fiddler a 50-spot to follow you and your date for the evening. The background soundtrack will make it feel as if you're in a movie. It's spontaneous, fun, and romantic.

17. GO TO DINNER AT A SUPERFANCY RESTAURANT. "During the meal, you're allowed to talk only about sexual fantasies," suggests Patricia Love, Ed.D., a relationship consultant and the author of *Hot*

Monogamy. "There's something very erotic about being public and being surreptitious about your sexuality." Bonus mission: Order foods that are delicious and lascivious at the same time.

18. GET COOKING. As with home improvement (see #12 on page 219), it's about the journey, not the result. "It's an opportunity to create something special as a couple," says celebrity chef and restaurateur Bobby Flay. "So the crème brûlée doesn't set. Who cares? It's just the two of you." See "What's for Dinner Tonight" at menshealth.com.

19. GO TO BARBADOS. Rich folks such as Prince Charles, Jerry Seinfeld, and Cindy Crawford stay at the Sandy Lane Hotel on the serene west side of the island, where a three-room penthouse costs up to $7,000 a night and the cheapest rooms during peak season are $950. But there's a less expensive way. Greenberg suggests renting a Toyota and driver for $200 a day, then heading south to the Silver Rock Hotel (246-428-2866), which goes for $120 a night with a balcony and full ocean view. The Silver Sands Beach, where world-champion windsurfers train, is just outside. Go between May and the end of December, the off-peak months, and most rates are discounted up to 50 percent. Don't leave without sampling the flying fish.

20. CHALLENGE HER TO STRIP PLAYSTATION. What's more fun than cleaving your partner's head off with a laser scimitar? "Competing with your partner in a playful environment can help you work out some aggressions," says Jennifer Worick, coauthor of *The Worst-Case Scenario Survival Handbook: Dating and Sex*. "Strip video gaming is fun and sexy. Every time a character is killed, you must remove a piece of clothing." For the ultimate in hot gaming action, try Dead or Alive Xtreme Beach Volleyball for Xbox. DOA has more T and A than any game out there—it's basically soft-core porn.

21. SPEND THE NIGHT IN AN IGLOO. For a thrilling, once-in-a-lifetime experience, you can't beat the Kakslauttanen Hotel and Igloo Village in the Finnish Laplands, well within the Arctic Circle. It ain't cheap. It ain't convenient. But you'll definitely get close as you huddle for warmth. Each igloo contains a bed made of snow draped with blankets and reindeer hides. Even when the mercury dips below −40°F outside, the igloos keep couples toasty at around 6°F to 8°F as they sip locally distilled Finlandia vodka and watch the aurora borealis light up the night. The Finns guarantee that any child conceived under the northern lights (best viewed September to April) will be male. See www.travel.fi/int/kakslauttanen for more information. Or build an igloo in your yard next time it snows. It's nearly as much fun.

22. GO TO AN ART MUSEUM. Forget the art; your mission is the art of foreplay. Stand close and speak in hushed tones about the exhibits . . . the other people . . . and what you want to do to each other when you get home. It's also nice to make the occasional soul-baring observation in a setting where it doesn't sound too lame. Plus, there are always at least a few naked pictures, some dark nooks and crannies, and a decent café.

23. GET NAKED! Make your own art—on each other. Pick up a chocolate tattoo set ($15) at early2bed.com. It includes a jar of chocolate body frosting, stencil sheets, and a paintbrush. Lick off.

24. MAKE OUT UNDER A WATERFALL. If you find yourself in Kauai, Hawaii, and the abundant natural beauty, welcoming locals, and crashing surf don't leave you feeling completely satisfied, there's something wrong with you. But if you need to spice things up, take an Air 1 Kauai helicopter to the bottom of a waterfall. They fly with the doors off, so every seat has a first-class view. One caveat: Air 1 Kauai also flies all the island's rescue missions; if they get a call, they'll drop you off wherever you are and come back later. Then again, where better to be stranded?

25. JUST MAKE OUT! Have a make-out date at least an hour long, says Joannides, with no below-the-belt contact. It's fun, teenage style!

Bathing Beauty

Find out how treating her like a princess can
make her treat you like a king

BY JENNIFER BENJAMIN

THE SHORTCUT to a woman's devotion: surprises. All the better if you can appeal to her caregiving instinct and turn it back on her in unexpected ways. She'll turn to mush if you treat her to an out-of-the-blue gesture that pampers her. "The key is to do something that takes thought and effort and is just for her," says Sandor Gardos, Ph.D., a sexologist for mypleasure.com. "If she thinks you're just trying to get her into bed, your plan will backfire." Here are some sexy surprises that will make her feel like royalty and pay off royally for you.

COME CLEAN. Light a few candles and fill a tub with hot water just before she gets home. Nothing says pampered like being bathed. Just don't forget the aphrodisiacs! Enhance the water with scented oils, either cucumber or a combination of banana and vanilla, says Alan Hirsch, M.D., neurological director of the Smell and Taste Treatment and Research Foundation in Chicago. Escorting her to the tub and helping her undress might be enough to encourage dirty bathing thoughts, and, Hirsch says, "these scents can increase vaginal blood-flow, heightening sexual arousal in women."

EAT IN. Instead of your standard takeout-and-TV evening, treat her to a bedroom picnic—complete with a blanket on the floor or spread over the bed. Open a bottle of wine (white or champagne is less of a stain hazard than red) and serve up some simple finger foods like sushi, dim sum (extra points if you can feed her with chopsticks), or even homemade English-muffin pizzas. "Making dinner plays to a woman's heart because it's one less thing she has to deal with when she gets home," says Carolyn Bushong, a psychotherapist and the author of *Bring Back the Man You Fell in Love With*. And the proximity to the bed makes it unique and especially sexy.

MAKE HER BED. Few words are sexier to women than "high thread count." Be sure to pay attention to the color scheme in her bedroom, and pick up a new sheet set with a thread count of 300 or more, in Turkish or Egyptian cotton. Then make her bed with the new stuff. Trust us—you'll be spending much more time there now.

PLAY DRESS-UP. Before your next night out, do a little role reversal and pick out the clothes you can't wait to see her in—and out of— later. Tell her you remember how good she looked the last time she wore that dress/blouse/cutoff concert shirt (extra points if you can recall when that was). "It shows her that you pay attention to how she looks and take note when she looks especially sexy," says Linda De Villers, Ph.D., a sex therapist and the author of *Love Skills*. "Most men aren't good at this, so it'll put you a step ahead of other guys."

QUICKIES

Her Muscles, Your Results

A great physique gets you in her door, but doesn't get you between the sheets, no matter how much she wants to see your serratus in action. For that, you need to get her body in the game. The best place to start is the sole, using these three reflexology tricks.

THUMB ROLL, PLEASE. Try this move from Bill Flocco, president of the American Academy of Reflexology: Support one of her feet in one hand while you use the fingers of the other hand to squeeze it gently and steadily. After a minute or so, place your thumb on the center of her sole and bend the thumb's knuckle back and forth across the foot without ever losing contact with her skin. This will send "stimulating signals" to her entire body.

DRAW HER IN. See the hollow beneath her anklebone? The one on the inside of her leg? Place your index finger there and, using light pressure, draw small circles within its boundaries. "That stimulates the reflex to the sex organs. It kind of wakes them up," says Michelle Kluck, president of BasicKnead.com and author of *Hands on Feet*.

HEAD OFF EXCUSES. Maybe she really does have a headache. If so, you'll need to focus on her big toe—the foot's equivalent of Excedrin. Take her toe between your index finger and thumb, and gently squeeze. Hold for 10 seconds, release, and repeat until she grabs your hand and moves it somewhere higher.

3 Ways to Jump-Start Your Wife

1. CHANGE YOUR SCENT. "Women's sense of smell is more sensitive, so if you change, she'll pay more attention," says Lou Paget, a sex educator in Los Angeles and the author of *365 Days of Sensational Sex*. It could be a new soap or antiperspirant. Or change your cologne. (Or start wearing some.) Researchers at the Monell Chemical Senses Center found that women were more receptive to scent than men, probably because scent plays an important role in female reproduction.

2. FIX HER DINNER. Or do a load of laundry. Or wash the dishes. Do anything before she has to ask—it will pull your sex life out of a rut. It'll be one less chore for her, and she'll feel special and want to reciprocate. "Seduction is about paying attention, and foreplay starts at 8 A.M.," Paget says.

3. GO ON A DATE. But not just to the local sushi hut. Find a quiet place with a big view; it encourages a larger perspective, says Peter Pearson, Ph.D., director of the Couples Institute in Menlo Park, California. Discuss what you want to create together. It's like a brainstorming meeting with no bad ideas. The only off-limits question: How are you gonna do that? There'll come a time for critical or analytical thinking, but not during this conversation. After everything's come out, let it sit for a week or two; then revisit and see what's still exciting. Do this once a year and take notes. Look at it as goal setting for the relationship.

SEX TEXTS

Hot Books

You can't tell a sex book by its nude cover models. So we did research. Some intriguing bits from new offerings:

• *Sex Talk* by Aline Zoldbrod, Ph.D., and Lauren Dockett. Enact a ban (on intercourse, kissing, or touching) to build tension, and at a specified time, end the ban with a bang.

• *The Complete Idiot's Guide to Amazing Sex*, 2nd edition, by Sari Locker. For you or her: Chill your mouth with ice water and go down. Then rinse with hot water and repeat.

• *Sexy Encounters* by Carole Pasahow. Set the alarm for the middle of the night, cuddle and fondle when it goes off, but go back to sleep. In the morning, "you'll wake up filled with desire," the author claims.

• *The Pocket Book of Sensational Orgasms* by Richard Craze. For G-spot glory, put two fingers in her vagina—at 11 o'clock and 1 o'clock—and stroke inward. As she climaxes, pull upward while pushing on her pubic bone with your other hand.

ASK THE GIRL
NEXT DOOR
The honest truth about women
from our lovely neighbor

Her Fickle Elmo
**Why is it that I can use the same sex moves with my wife and on
some nights they make her orgasm and on other nights they don't?**
—NICK, BROOKLYN, NEW YORK

I wish women's bodies were more like telephones: Dial the right numbers, and bells start ringing. The reality is that if our minds are preoc-
cupied—with work, body-image issues, relationship problems,
whatever—less blood will flow to our genitals, making them less sensitive. But variety always helps. If you used a swirl last night, try a
figure eight this evening.

Implanted in her Head
**My girlfriend has been talking about getting breast implants. I love
her as is but respect that it's her body and her decision. What's a
guy to say?**   —ANONYMOUS

Yes, it's her rack to ruin; but since you're the main handler of her
hooters, your opinion can have a major impact. What your girlfriend
really wants isn't bigger boobs; it's to be happy with and proud of her
body. That's something you can help her with, to a point; then a
therapist needs to take over. Keep showering her natural assets with
sincere praise. Rub, lick, and kiss them as if they're ice cream cones
and you're Omar Sharif stumbling out of the desert. And gently remind her that fake breasts can easily go from novel playthings to annoying burdens. Even the people who make them admit that implants
aren't lifetime medical devices, which means additional surgery down
the line.

   For unbiased info about implants, visit fda.gov/cdrh/breastimplants.

Getting to O

My girlfriend has never had an orgasm during intercourse. What should I try?   —ANONYMOUS

Everything. But start with this: Lay her down on her stomach and slowly rub massage oil into her shoulders and back. Work your way down her body, spending extra time massaging her bottom. Turn her over and rub oil onto every inch of her skin other than her breasts and pubic region. Remember, the longer you tease, the better. Finally, lick and kiss her nipples while your hand slides between her legs. Using a circular motion, stroke her clitoris gently with the pads of your fingers, increasing the pressure slightly every few minutes. After a good 10 minutes of rubbing, slide the index finger of your other hand inside her, up against the inside front of her vagina. Press and release as if you're gently pumping up a pair of early-'90s basketball sneakers. After several minutes, maneuver her on top of you cowgirl style, and, guiding her hips with your hands, encourage her to grind back and forth against your abdomen while your penis is inside her. At this point she's in the position that makes most women orgasm the fastest, and after all that stimulation, she'll be as ready as ever to let go.

Break the Fake

I know my girlfriend is faking orgasms. How do I talk to her about it?
—ANONYMOUS

Don't let on that you know. Instead, tell her you can't figure out exactly what makes her orgasm, but you want to learn. Refuse to accept cop-outs like "Oh, you already do a great job." Ask her to show and tell you what you need to do, and make it clear that you're eager to work on this project for a while. Most women fake orgasms because they're embarrassed about how much time (20 minutes plus) and friction (think sanding a wood floor) it takes to score the real deal.

INDEX

<u>Underscored</u> page references indicate boxed text.